TOP 500

SHOPS, RESTAURANTS, ARTS & NIGHTLIFE

BOSTON

The Ultimate Travel Guide
to Boston City

BOSTON CITY GUIDE 2022
Shops, Restaurants, Arts, Entertainment & Nightlife

© David R. Schorer
© E.G.P. Editorial

Printed in USA.

ISBN-13: 9798504346748

INDEX

BOSTON CITY GUIDE

Shops, Restaurants, Attractions, Entertainment & Nightlife

*This directory is dedicated to Boston Business Owners and Managers
who provide the experience that the locals and tourists enjoy.
Thanks you very much for all that you do and thank for being the "People Choice".*

*Thanks to everyone that posts their reviews online and
the amazing reviews sites that make our life easier.*

*The places listed in this book are the most positively reviewed
and recommended by locals and travelers from around the world.*

*Thank you for your time and enjoy the directory that is
designed with locals and tourist in mind!*

TOP 500 SHOPS

Most Recommended by Locals & Trevelers
Ranking (from #1 to #500)

#1
Sleep-A-Rama
Category: Mattresses
Average price: Modest
Area: Fenway
Address: 1260 Boylston St
Boston, MA 02115
Phone: (617) 266-8863

#2
Sarra
Category: Makeup Artists,
Cosmetics, Beauty Supply
Average price: Expensive
Area: South Boston
Address: 840 Summer St
Boston, MA 02127
Phone: (617) 269-8999

#3
Salmagundi
Category: Accessories, Hats
Average price: Modest
Area: Jamaica Plain
Address: 765 Centre St
Boston, MA 02130
Phone: (617) 522-5047

#4
Goorin Bros.
Category: Accessories, Hats
Average price: Modest
Area: Back Bay
Address: 130 Newbury Street
Boston, MA 02116
Phone: (617) 247-4287

#5
Ancient Arts
Category: Piercing, Jewelry
Average price: Modest
Area: Allston/Brighton
Address: 1018 Commonwealth Ave
Boston, MA 02215
Phone: (617) 466-9927

#6
Yuri's Watches
Category: Watches, Watch Repair
Average price: Inexpensive
Area: Back Bay
Address: 142 Newbury St
Boston, MA 02116
Phone: (617) 536-8895

#7
Bobby From Boston
Category: Vintage, Men's Clothing
Average price: Modest
Area: South End
Address: 19 Thayer St
Boston, MA 02118
Phone: (617) 423-9299

#8
Black Ink
Category: Cards, Stationery,
Bookstore, Kitchen & Bath
Average price: Expensive
Area: Beacon Hill
Address: 101 Charles St
Boston, MA 02114
Phone: (617) 723-3883

#9
Brattle Book Shop
Category: Bookstore
Average price: Inexpensive
Area: Downtown
Address: 9 West St
Boston, MA 02111
Phone: (617) 542-0210

#10
Follain
Category: Cosmetics, Beauty Supply
Average price: Expensive
Area: South End
Address: 53 Dartmouth St
Boston, MA 02116
Phone: (857) 284-7078

#11
INTIMACY - bra fit stylists
Category: Lingerie, Women's Clothing
Average price: Expensive
Area: Back Bay
Address: 100 Huntington Avenue
Boston, MA 02116
Phone: (857) 277-7887

#12
lululemon athletica
Category: Sports Wear,
Women's Clothing
Average price: Expensive
Area: Back Bay
Address: 776 Boylston St
Boston, MA 02116
Phone: (617) 262-2030

#13
Galvin-ized Headwear
Category: Accessories, Hats
Average price: Expensive
Area: South End
Address: 450 Harrison Ave
Boston, MA 02118
Phone: (617) 834-2910

#14
Marathon Sports
Category: Shoe Store, Sports Wear
Average price: Modest
Area: Back Bay
Address: 671 Boylston St
Boston, MA 02116
Phone: (617) 267-4774

#15
Warby Parker
Category: Eyewear, Opticians
Average price: Inexpensive
Area: Back Bay
Address: 83 Newbury St
Boston, MA 02116
Phone: (508) 658-7444

#16
Riccardi
Category: Men's Clothing,
Women's Clothing
Average price: Exclusive
Area: Back Bay
Address: 116 Newbury St
Boston, MA 02116
Phone: (617) 266-3158

#17
Superior Diamond Setting
Category: Jewelry
Average price: Inexpensive
Area: Downtown
Address: 333 Washington St
Boston, MA 02108
Phone: (617) 723-7236

#18
Shomali & Richmond Optometrists
Category: Eyewear, Opticians
Average price: Modest
Area: Downtown
Address: 101 Tremont St
Boston, MA 02108
Phone: (617) 426-3236

#19
Bostonwood
Category: Home Decor, Furniture Store
Average price: Modest
Area: Allston/Brighton
Address: 1117 Commonwealth Ave
Boston, MA 02215
Phone: (617) 783-0274

#20
Back Bay Hardware
Category: Hardware Store
Average price: Modest
Area: Back Bay
Address: 233 Newbury St
Boston, MA 02116
Phone: (617) 536-0913

#21
Uniform
Category: Men's Clothing
Average price: Expensive
Area: South End
Address: 511 Tremont St
Boston, MA 02118
Phone: (617) 247-2360

#22
Crate & Barrel
Category: Furniture Store,
Home Decor, Kitchen & Bath
Average price: Modest
Area: Back Bay
Address: 777 Boylston St
Boston, MA 02116
Phone: (617) 262-8700

#23
Commonwealth Books
Category: Bookstore
Average price: Modest
Area: Downtown
Address: 9 Spring Ln
Boston, MA 02109
Phone: (617) 338-6328

#24
Rugg Road Paper Co
Category: Art Supplies,
Cards, Stationery
Average price: Expensive
Area: Beacon Hill
Address: 105 Charles St
Boston, MA 02114
Phone: (617) 742-0002

#25
Cole-Haan Store
Category: Shoe Store
Average price: Expensive
Area: Back Bay
Address: 109 Newbury St
Boston, MA 02116
Phone: (617) 536-7826

#26
Hudson
Category: Furniture Store
Average price: Expensive
Area: South End
Address: 12 Union Park St
Boston, MA 02118
Phone: (617) 292-0900

#27
Lipstick
Category: Women's Clothing
Average price: Modest
Area: Back Bay
Address: 293 Newbury St
Boston, MA 02115
Phone: (617) 267-6900

#28
Sabon
Category: Cosmetics, Beauty Supply
Average price: Expensive
Area: Back Bay
Address: 129 Newbury St
Boston, MA 02116
Phone: (617) 236-1931

#29
Agent Provocateur
Category: Lingerie
Average price: Exclusive
Area: Back Bay
Address: 123 Newbury St
Boston, MA 02116
Phone: (617) 267-0229

#30
Patch NYC
Category: Home Decor,
Jewelry, Antiques
Average price: Modest
Area: South End
Address: 46 Waltham St
Boston, MA 02118
Phone: (617) 426-0592

#31
REI
Category: Outdoor Gear, Sports Wear
Average price: Expensive
Area: Fenway
Address: 401 Park Dr
Boston, MA 02215
Phone: (617) 236-0746

#32
Tadpole
Category: Toy Store,
Baby Gear & Furniture
Average price: Expensive
Area: South End
Address: 58 Clarendon St
Boston, MA 02116
Phone: (617) 778-1788

#33
The Fairy Shop
Category: Jewelry, Bookstore
Average price: Modest
Area: Back Bay
Address: 272 Newbury St
Boston, MA 02116
Phone: (617) 262-2520

#34
Grey's Fabric and Notions
Category: Fabric Store
Average price: Modest ✓
Area: South End
Address: 450 Harrison Ave
Boston, MA 02118
Phone: (617) 338-4739

#35
Helen's Leather Shop
Category: Leather Goods, Shoe Store
Average price: Modest
Area: Beacon Hill
Address: 110 Charles St Ste 1
Boston, MA 02114
Phone: (617) 742-2077

#36
Shake The Tree
Category: Fashion, Jewelry
Average price: Expensive
Area: North End
Address: 67 Salem St
Boston, MA 02113
Phone: (617) 742-0484

#37
Newbury Comics
Category: Comic Books,
Music & DVDs, Vinyl Records
Average price: Modest
Area: Back Bay
Address: 332 Newbury St
Boston, MA 02115
Phone: (617) 236-4930

#38
Acquire
Category: Home Decor
Average price: Modest
Area: North End
Address: 61 Salem St
Boston, MA 02113
Phone: (857) 362-7380

#39
Crush Boutique
Category: Women's Clothing,
Jewelry, Accessories ✓
Average price: Expensive
Area: Beacon Hill
Address: 131 Charles St
Boston, MA 02114
Phone: (617) 720-0010

#40
Trident Booksellers & Café
Category: Bookstore,
Breakfast & Brunch, Sandwiches
Average price: Modest
Area: Back Bay
Address: 338 Newbury St
Boston, MA 02115
Phone: (617) 267-8688

#41
Orchard Skate Shop
Category: Sporting Goods, Shoe Store
Average price: Modest
Area: Allston/Brighton
Address: 156 Harvard Ave
Boston, MA 02134
Phone: (617) 782-7777

#42
Sephora
Category: Cosmetics, Beauty Supply
Average price: Modest
Area: Back Bay
Address: 800 Boylston St
Boston, MA 02199
Phone: (617) 262-4200

#43
Boston Platinum
Category: Jewelry
Average price: Modest
Area: Downtown
Address: 333 Washington St
Boston, MA 02108
Phone: (617) 504-3531

#44
Back Bay Bicycles
Category: Bikes
Average price: Expensive
Area: Back Bay
Address: 362 Commonwealth Ave
Boston, MA 02115
Phone: (617) 247-2336

#45
Winmil Fabric
Category: Fabric Store
Average price: Modest
Area: Chinatown
Address: 111 Chauncy St
Boston, MA 02111
Phone: (617) 542-1815

#46
9tailors
Category: Men's Clothing,
Women's Clothing
Average price: Modest
Area: Downtown
Address: 24 School St
Boston, MA 02108
Phone: (617) 286-6135

#47
Marc Jacobs
Category: Men's Clothing, Women's
Clothing, Accessories
Average price: Expensive
Area: Back Bay
Address: 81 Newbury St
Boston, MA 02116
Phone: (617) 425-0404

#48
Bromfield Camera Co
Category: Electronics,
Photography Store&Service
Average price: Expensive
Area: Downtown
Address: 10 Bromfield St
Boston, MA 02108
Phone: (617) 426-5230

#49
Fresh
Category: Cosmetics, Beauty Supply
Average price: Expensive
Area: Back Bay
Address: 121 Newbury Street
Boston, MA 02116
Phone: (617) 421-1212

#50
Copley Place
Category: Shopping Center
Average price: Exclusive
Area: Back Bay
Address: 110 Huntington Ave
Boston, MA 02116
Phone: (617) 262-6600

#51
Lucky Brand Jeans
Category: Fashion
Average price: Expensive
Area: Back Bay
Address: 229 Newbury St Bsmt
Boston, MA 02116
Phone: (617) 236-0102

#52
KitchenWares by Blackstones
Category: Kitchen & Bath
Average price: Modest
Area: Back Bay
Address: 215 Newbury St
Boston, MA 02116
Phone: (857) 366-4237

#53
Community Bicycle Supply
Category: Bikes
Average price: Modest
Area: South End
Address: 496 Tremont St
Boston, MA 02118
Phone: (617) 542-8623

#54
Bettie Page Clothing
Category: Women's Clothing
Average price: Expensive
Area: Back Bay
Address: 32 Newbury St
Boston, MA 02116
Phone: (857) 233-5016

#55
MarsHall
Category: Department Store
Average price: Modest
Area: Back Bay
Address: 500 Boylston St
Boston, MA 02116
Phone: (617) 262-6066

#56
**Aveda Environmental
Lifestyle Store**
Category: Massage, Nail Salon,
Cosmetics, Beauty Supply
Average price: Expensive
Area: Back Bay
Address: 100 Huntington Ave
Boston, MA 02116
Phone: (617) 236-1917

#57
In-Jean-Ius
Category: Women's Clothing
Average price: Expensive
Area: North End
Address: 441 Hanover St
Boston, MA 02228
Phone: (617) 523-5326

#58
Rick Walker's
Category: Vintage
Average price: Modest
Area: Back Bay
Address: 306 Newbury St
Boston, MA 02115
Phone: (617) 482-7426

#59
Boomerangs Special Edition
Category: Thrift Store, Vintage
Average price: Modest
Area: South End
Address: 1407 Washington St
Boston, MA 02118
Phone: (617) 456-0996

#60
Twentieth Century
Category: Antiques
Average price: Expensive
Address: 73 Charles St
Boston, MA 02108
Phone: (617) 742-1031

#61
Kiehl's Since 1851
Category: Cosmetics, Beauty Supply
Average price: Expensive
Area: Back Bay
Address: 112 Newbury St
Boston, MA 02116
Phone: (617) 247-1777

#62
Faneuil Hall Marketplace
Category: Shopping Center,
Fruits & Veggies, American
Average price: Modest
Area: Financial District
Address: 4 S Market Bldg
Boston, MA 02109
Phone: (617) 523-1300

#63
The Boston Bed Company
Category: Mattresses, Furniture Store
Average price: Modest
Area: Allston/Brighton
Address: 1113 Commonwealth Ave
Boston, MA 02215
Phone: (617) 782-3830

#64
Small Pleasures
Category: Jewelry, Antiques
Average price: Expensive
Area: Back Bay
Address: 142 Newbury St
Boston, MA 02116
Phone: (617) 267-7371

#65
The North Face
Category: Outdoor Gear, Sports Wear
Average price: Expensive
Area: Back Bay
Address: 326 Newbury St
Boston, MA 02115
Phone: (617) 536-8060

#66
Eyes Over Copley
Category: Eyewear, Opticians
Average price: Expensive
Area: Back Bay
Address: 10 Huntington Ave
Boston, MA 02116
Phone: (617) 859-0630

#67
Mega Mobile Boston
Category: Mobile Phones,
Mobile Phone Repair
Average price: Modest
Area: Downtown
Address: 278 Washington St
Boston, MA 02108
Phone: (617) 573-0073

#68
**It's a Man's World
Men's Image Consulting**
Category: Men's Clothing
Average price: Modest
Area: East Boston
Address: Back Bay
Boston, MA 02101
Phone: (339) 933-0785

#69
Twilight
Category: Women's Clothing
Average price: Expensive
Area: Downtown
Address: 12 Fleet St
Boston, MA 02228
Phone: (617) 523-8008

closed

#70
Barneys New York
Category: Accessories, Shoe Store
Average price: Exclusive
Area: Back Bay
Address: 100 Huntington Ave
Boston, MA 02116
Phone: (617) 385-3300

closed

#71
Flair Brides + Maids
Category: Bridal, Wedding Planning
Average price: Expensive
Area: Back Bay
Address: 140 Newbury St
Boston, MA 02116
Phone: (617) 247-2828

#72
South End Athletic Company
Category: Sports Wear
Average price: Modest
Area: South End
Address: 652 Tremont St
Boston, MA 02118
Phone: (617) 391-0897

#73
DSW Designer Shoe Warehouse
Category: Shoe Store
Average price: Modest
Area: Downtown
Address: 385 Washington St
Boston, MA 02108
Phone: (617) 556-0052

#74
Flat of the Hill
Category: Accessories, Home Decor
Average price: Expensive
Area: Beacon Hill
Address: 60 Charles St
Boston, MA 02114
Phone: (617) 619-9977

#75
The Beauty Mark
Category: Cosmetics, Beauty Supply,
Makeup Artists
Average price: Expensive
Area: Beacon Hill
Address: 33 Charles St
Boston, MA 02114
Phone: (617) 720-1555

#76
Paper Source
Category: Cards, Stationery,
Art Supplies
Average price: Modest
Area: Back Bay
Address: 338 Boylston St
Boston, MA 02116
Phone: (617) 536-3444

#77
Anthropologie
Category: Home Decor, Shoe Store,
Women's Clothing
Average price: Expensive
Area: Back Bay
Address: 203 Newbury St
Boston, MA 02116
Phone: (617) 262-0545

#78
Artists For Humanity Epicenter
Category: Venues, Event Space,
Art Gallery
Average price: Modest
Area: South Boston
Address: 100 West Second St
Boston, MA 02127
Phone: (617) 268-7620

#79
Madewell
Category: Women's Clothing,
Accessories, Shoe Store
Average price: Expensive
Area: Back Bay
Address: 329 Newbury Street
Boston, MA 02115
Phone: (617) 424-0904

#80
Wellesley Optical
Category: Eyewear, Opticians
Average price: Modest
Area: Back Bay
Address: 216 Newbury St
Boston, MA 02116
Phone: (617) 247-2020

#81
1154 Lill Studio
Category: Accessories
Average price: Expensive
Area: Back Bay
Address: 220 Newbury St
Boston, MA 02116
Phone: (617) 247-1154

#82
Boston Center for the Arts
Category: Art Gallery, Performing Arts,
Venues, Event Space
Average price: Modest
Area: South End
Address: 539 Tremont St
Boston, MA 02116
Phone: (617) 426-5000

#83
Gifted
Category: Jewelry, Gift Shop
Average price: Modest
Area: South End
Address: 2 Dartmouth St
Boston, MA 02116
Phone: (617) 716-9924

#84
The Closet
Category: Vintage,
Women's Clothing
Average price: Expensive
Area: Back Bay
Address: 175 Newbury St
Boston, MA 02116
Phone: (617) 536-1919

#85
Closet Connection
Category: Thrift Store, Vintage,
Women's Clothing
Average price: Modest
Area: South Boston
Address: 553 E Broadway St
Boston, MA 02127
Phone: (617) 268-2949

#86
Bonobos Guideshop
Category: Men's Clothing,
Formal Wear, Swimwear
Average price: Expensive
Area: Back Bay
Address: 283 Dartmouth St
Boston, MA 02116
Phone: (857) 263-7340

#87
Coco Baby
Category: Children's Clothing, Toy Store
Average price: Modest
Area: South End
Address: 1636 Washington St
Boston, MA 02118
Phone: (617) 247-2229

#88
Luke Adams Gifting Co
Category: Gift Shop, Art Classes
Average price: Modest
Area: South End
Address: 565 Columbus Ave
Boston, MA 02118
Phone: (781) 241-3187

#89
Lester Harry's
Category: Children's Clothing,
Baby Gear & Furniture
Average price: Expensive
Area: Back Bay
Address: 115 Newbury Street
Boston, MA 02116
Phone: (617) 927-5400

#90
Emporio Armani Boutique
Category: Fashion
Average price: Exclusive
Area: Back Bay
Address: 2 Copley Pl
Boston, MA 02116
Phone: (617) 262-7300

#91
Wolford
Category: Women's Clothing, Lingerie
Average price: Expensive
Area: Back Bay
Address: 100 Huntington Ave
Boston, MA 02116
Phone: (617) 236-5070

#92
Mayfair On the Hill
Category: Cosmetics, Beauty Supply,
Hair Salon
Average price: Expensive
Area: Beacon Hill
Address: 81 W Cedar St
Boston, MA 02114
Phone: (617) 742-6662

#93
Bead + Fiber
Category: Art Supplies, Knitting Supplies
Average price: Modest
Area: South End
Address: 460 Harrison Ave
Boston, MA 02118
Phone: (617) 426-2323

#94
Bedrosian Jewelry
Category: Jewelry
Average price: Modest
Area: Downtown
Address: 333 Washington St
Boston, MA 02108
Phone: (617) 227-9452

#95
Karli Jewelers
Category: Jewelry
Average price: Modest
Area: Downtown
Address: 333 Washington St
Boston, MA 02108
Phone: (617) 523-0435

#96
Vera Bradley
Category: Outlet Store
Average price: Modest
Area: Back Bay
Address: 800 Boylston St, Ste 149
Boston, MA 02199
Phone: (617) 236-0770

#97
Britt Ryan
Category: Women's Clothing
Average price: Expensive
Area: Back Bay
Address: 291 Newbury St
Boston, MA 02115
Phone: (857) 284-7196

#98
H&M
Category: Men's Clothing,
Women's Clothing, Accessories
Average price: Inexpensive
Area: Downtown
Address: 350 Washington St
Boston, MA 02108
Phone: (855) 466-7467

#99
Hermes
Category: Men's Clothing,
Women's Clothing, Accessories
Average price: Exclusive
Area: Back Bay
Address: 320 Boylston St
Boston, MA 02116
Phone: (617) 482-8707

#100
Green Cross Pharmacy
Category: Drugstore
Average price: Inexpensive
Area: North End
Address: 393 Hanover St
Boston, MA 02113
Phone: (617) 227-3728

#101
Lux Bond & Green
Category: Jewelry, Watches
Average price: Exclusive
Area: Back Bay
Address: 416 Boylston St
Boston, MA 02116
Phone: (617) 266-4747

#102
The Coach Store
Category: Leather Goods
Average price: Expensive
Area: Back Bay
Address: 100 Huntington Ave
Ste 16, Boston, MA 02116
Phone: (617) 262-2063

#103
Bromfield Pen Shop
Category: Cards, Stationery
Average price: Expensive
Area: Downtown
Address: 5 Bromfield St
Boston, MA 02108
Phone: (617) 482-9053

#104
John Fluevog
Category: Shoe Store
Average price: Expensive
Area: Back Bay
Address: 302 Newbury St
Boston, MA 02115
Phone: (617) 266-1079

#105
Felicity Sweets
Category: Candy Store, Jewelry,
Flowers, Gifts
Average price: Modest
Area: South End
Address: 579 Tremont St
Boston, MA 02118
Phone: (617) 262-0707

#106
Calypso
Category: Women's Clothing
Average price: Expensive
Area: Back Bay
Address: 114 Newbury St
Boston, MA 02116
Phone: (617) 421-1887

#107
Turtle
Category: Women's Clothing
Average price: Expensive
Area: South End
Address: 619 Tremont St
Boston, MA 02118
Phone: (617) 266-2610

#108
Exotic Flowers
Category: Florist
Average price: Modest
Area: Roslindale
Address: 609 American Legion Hwy
Boston, MA 02131
Phone: (617) 247-2000

#109
CVS/Pharmacy
Category: Drugstore
Average price: Modest
Area: Back Bay
Address: 285 Columbus Ave
Boston, MA 02116
Phone: (617) 236-8538

#110
Michelle Willey
Category: Home Decor
Average price: Modest
Area: South End
Address: 8 Union Park St
Boston, MA 02118
Phone: (617) 424-6700

#111
Banana Republic
Category: Sports Wear
Average price: Modest
Area: Back Bay
Address: 4 Copley Pl
Boston, MA 02116
Phone: (617) 424-7817

#112
Pinkyotto
Category: Women's Clothing
Average price: Expensive
Area: Back Bay
Address: 156 Newbury St
Boston, MA 02116
Phone: (617) 236-1238

#113
The Shop At Prudential Center
Category: Shopping Center
Average price: Expensive
Area: Back Bay
Address: 800 Boylston St
Boston, MA 02199
Phone: (617) 236-3100

#114
Intermix
Category: Women's Clothing
Average price: Expensive
Area: Back Bay
Address: 186 Newbury St
Boston, MA 02116
Phone: (617) 236-5172

#115
So Good Jewelry
Category: Jewelry
Average price: Inexpensive
Area: Downtown
Address: 426 Washington St
Boston, MA 02108
Phone: (617) 542-0573

#116
City Sports
Category: Sporting Goods
Average price: Modest
Area: Back Bay
Address: 480 Boylston St
Boston, MA 02116
Phone: (617) 267-3900

#117
Moxie
Category: Shoe Store
Average price: Expensive
Area: Beacon Hill
Address: 51 Charles St
Boston, MA 02108
Phone: (617) 557-9991

#118
Flock
Category: Women's Clothing, Jewelry
Average price: Modest
Area: South End
Address: 274 Shawmut Ave
Boston, MA 02118
Phone: (617) 391-0222

#119
Lord & Taylor
Category: Department Store,
Men's Clothing, Women's Clothing
Average price: Modest
Area: Back Bay
Address: 760 Boylston St.
Boston, MA 02199
Phone: (617) 262-6000

#120
Walgreens
Category: Drugstore
Average price: Modest
Area: Downtown
Address: 24 School St
Boston, MA 02110
Phone: (617) 372-8156

#121
Eastern Mountain Sports
Category: Outdoor Gear, Sports Wear
Average price: Modest
Area: Allston/Brighton
Address: 1041 Commonwealth Av
Boston, MA 02215
Phone: (617) 254-4250

#122
Ilex Designs
Category: Florist
Average price: Modest
Area: South End
Address: 73 Berkeley St
Boston, MA 02116
Phone: (617) 422-0300

#123
SOWA Artists Guild
Category: Art Gallery
Average price: Modest
Area: South End
Address: 450 Harrison Ave
Boston, MA 02228
Phone: (978) 337-4191

#124
Tiffany & Co
Category: Jewelry
Average price: Exclusive
Area: Back Bay
Address: 4 Copley Pl
Boston, MA 02116
Phone: (617) 266-0052

#125
The Hempest
Category: Tobacco Shop,
Men's Clothing, Women's Clothing
Average price: Expensive
Area: Back Bay
Address: 207 Newbury St
Boston, MA 02116
Phone: (617) 421-9944

#126
New Balance Boston
Category: Sports Wear
Average price: Modest
Area: Back Bay
Address: 583 Boylston St
Boston, MA 02116
Phone: (617) 266-1583

#127
Sabella Couture
Category: Bridal
Average price: Expensive
Area: Downtown
Address: 151 Tremont St
Boston, MA 02111
Phone: (617) 426-8686

#128
Cuffs & Collars
Category: Men's Clothing
Average price: Expensive
Area: Downtown
Address: 9 Water St
Boston, MA 02109
Phone: (617) 720-2833

#129
Minter & Richter Designs
Category: Bridal, Jewelry
Average price: Modest
Area: Dorchester
Address: 2 Ainsley St
Boston, MA 02122
Phone: (617) 265-9659

#130
Dajuli Sparkles
Category: Jewelry
Average price: Modest
Area: Back Bay
Address: 304 Newbury St
Boston, MA 02115
Phone: (617) 572-2040

#131
Chanel Boutique
Category: Cosmetics, Beauty Supply
Average price: Exclusive
Area: Back Bay
Address: 6 Newbury St
Boston, MA 02116
Phone: (617) 859-0055

#132
Cohen's Fashion Optical
Category: Eyewear, Opticians
Average price: Modest
Area: Back Bay
Address: 607 Boylston St
Boston, MA 02116
Phone: (617) 236-5500

#133
Blackstone's Of Beacon Hill
Category: Cards, Stationery,
Home Decor, Jewelry
Average price: Modest
Area: Beacon Hill
Address: 46 Charles St
Boston, MA 02114
Phone: (617) 227-4646

#134
Burberry
Category: Fashion
Average price: Exclusive
Area: Back Bay
Address: 2 Newbury St
Boston, MA 02116
Phone: (617) 236-1000

#135
EB Horn & Co
Category: Jewelry, Watches, Bridal
Average price: Expensive
Area: Downtown
Address: 429 Washington St
Boston, MA 02108
Phone: (617) 542-3902

#136
Christian Dior
Category: Fashion
Average price: Exclusive
Area: Back Bay
Address: 100 Huntington Ave
Boston, MA 02116
Phone: (617) 927-7577

#137
Society of Arts, Crafts
Category: Arts, Crafts, Art Gallery
Average price: Modest
Area: Back Bay
Address: 175 Newbury St
Boston, MA 02116
Phone: (617) 266-1810

#138
MiniLuxe
Category: Nail Salon, Hair Removal,
Cosmetics, Beauty Supply
Average price: Expensive
Area: Back Bay
Address: 296 Newbury St
Boston, MA 02115
Phone: (857) 362-7444

#139
Jack Spade
Category: Accessories
Average price: Expensive
Area: Back Bay
Address: 129 Newbury St
Boston, MA 02116
Phone: (617) 536-0528

#140
Steven Alan
Category: Women's Clothing,
Men's Clothing
Average price: Exclusive
Area: Back Bay
Address: 172 Newbury St
Boston, MA 02116
Phone: (617) 398-2640

#141
Around the Corner
Category: Framing, Art Gallery
Average price: Expensive
Area: South End
Address: 637 Tremont St
Boston, MA 02118
Phone: (617) 266-1800

#142
Ars Libri
Category: Art Gallery, Bookstore
Average price: Modest
Area: South End
Address: 500 Harrison Ave
Boston, MA 02118
Phone: (617) 357-5212

#143
Vibram FiveFingers
Category: Shoe Store
Average price: Modest
Area: Back Bay
Address: 292 Newbury St
Boston, MA 02115
Phone: (857) 263-8508

#144
Fresco Flowers
Category: Florist
Average price: Modest
Area: Back Bay
Address: 145 Dartmouth St
Boston, MA 02116
Phone: (617) 228-0500

#145
Sisters Jewelry
Category: Jewelry
Average price: Modest
Area: Downtown
Address: 333 Washington St
Boston, MA 02108
Phone: (617) 720-4983

#146
Front
Category: Home Decor, Cards, Stationery
Average price: Expensive
Area: Waterfront, South Boston
Address: 25 Channel Center St
Boston, MA 02210
Phone: (857) 362-7289

#147
Bed Bath & Beyond
Category: Home & Garden
Average price: Modest
Area: Fenway
Address: 401 Park Dr
Boston, MA 02215
Phone: (617) 536-1090

#148
SoWa Vintage Market
Category: Vintage
Average price: Modest
Area: South End
Address: 460 C Harrison Ave
Boston, MA 02118
Phone: (800) 403-8305

#149
Fenway Pharmacy
Category: Drugstore
Average price: Exclusive
Area: Fenway
Address: 1340 Boylston St
Boston, MA 02215
Phone: (617) 927-6330

#150
International Poster Gallery
Category: Art Gallery
Average price: Expensive
Area: Back Bay
Address: 205 Newbury St
Boston, MA 02116
Phone: (617) 375-0076

#151
Diesel
Category: Women's Clothing,
Men's Clothing,Accessories
Average price: Expensive
Area: Back Bay
Address: 339 Newbury St
Boston, MA 02116
Phone: (617) 424-6555

#152
Louis Boston
Category: Department Store,
Men's Clothing, Women's Clothing
Average price: Exclusive
Area: Waterfront, South Boston
Address: 60 Northern Ave
Boston, MA 02210
Phone: (617) 262-6100

#153
LIT on Newbury
Category: Women's Clothing, Jewelry
Average price: Modest
Area: Back Bay
Address: 223 Newbury St
Boston, MA 02116
Phone: (617) 421-8637

#154
Rouvalis Flowers
Category: Florist
Average price: Expensive
Area: Beacon Hill
Address: 40 W Cedar St
Boston, MA 02108
Phone: (617) 720-2266

#155
Eddie Bauer
Category: Men's Clothing,
Women's Clothing, Outlet Store
Average price: Modest
Area: Downtown
Address: 500 Washington St
Boston, MA 02111
Phone: (617) 423-4722

#156
Good
Category: Jewelry, Antiques, Home Decor,
Accessories, Furniture Store
Average price: Expensive
Area: Beacon Hill
Address: 133 Charles St
Boston, MA 02114
Phone: (617) 722-9200

#157
Red Sox Team Store
Category: Sporting Goods
Average price: Expensive
Area: Fenway
Address: 19 Yawkey Way
Boston, MA 02215
Phone: (800) 336-9299

#158
French Connection
Category: Men's Clothing,
Women's Clothing
Average price: Expensive
Area: Back Bay
Address: 206 Newbury St
Boston, MA 02116
Phone: (617) 247-1301

#159
Reiss
Category: Fashion
Average price: Expensive
Area: Back Bay
Address: 132 Newbury St
Boston, MA 02228
Phone: (617) 262-5800

#160
Newbury Comics
Category: Music & DVDs, Comic Books
Average price: Modest
Area: North End
Address: 1 N Marketplace, Ste 366
Boston, MA 02109
Phone: (617) 248-9992

#161
The Red Wagon
Category: Children's Clothing
Average price: Expensive
Area: Beacon Hill
Address: 69 Charles St
Boston, MA 02114
Phone: (617) 523-9402

#162
Green Side Up Gallery
Category: Tobacco Shop
Average price: Modest
Area: Allston/Brighton
Address: 202 Harvard Ave
Boston, MA 02134
Phone: (617) 487-4882

#163
Ocean Time
Category: Watches, Watch Repair
Average price: Inexpensive
Area: Back Bay
Address: 800 Boylston St
Boston, MA 02199
Phone: (617) 236-0601

#164
M.A.C. Cosmetics
Category: Cosmetics, Beauty Supply
Average price: Expensive
Area: Downtown
Address: 450 Washington St
Boston, MA 02111
Phone: (617) 357-3000

#165
T.J. Maxx
Category: Department Store
Average price: Modest
Area: Downtown
Address: 350 Washington St
Boston, MA 02108
Phone: (617) 695-2424

#166
Jonathan Adler
Category: Home Decor
Average price: Expensive
Area: Back Bay
Address: 129 Newbury St
Boston, MA 02116
Phone: (617) 437-0018

#167
Pandora Jewelery
Category: Jewelry
Average price: Expensive
Area: Back Bay
Address: 800 Boyston St
Boston, MA 02199
Phone: (617) 927-5480

#168
Michele Mercaldo Jewelry
Category: Jewelry
Average price: Expensive
Area: South End
Address: 276 Shawmut Ave
Boston, MA 02118
Phone: (617) 350-7909

#169
Petalena
Category: Florist
Average price: Modest
Area: Jamaica Plain
Address: Boston, MA 02130
Phone: (978) 884-0868

#170
Amoroso Jewelers
Category: Jewelry
Average price: Modest
Area: Beacon Hill
Address: 333 Washington St
Boston, MA 02108
Phone: (617) 742-9900

#171
Thom Brown Shoes
Category: Shoe Store
Average price: Modest
Area: Back Bay
Address: 331 Newbury St
Boston, MA 02115
Phone: (617) 266-8722

#172
Second Time Around
Category: Women's Clothing,
Vintage
Average price: Modest
Area: Back Bay
Address: 219 Newbury St
Boston, MA 02228
Phone: (617) 266-1113

#173
L J Peretti Co
Category: Tobacco Shop
Average price: Modest
Area: Back Bay
Address: 2 1/2 Park Sq
Boston, MA 02116
Phone: (617) 482-0218

#174
So Good Jewelry
Category: Jewelry
Average price: Modest
Area: Back Bay
Address: 349 Newbury St
Boston, MA 02215
Phone: (617) 259-1053

#175
Puma
Category: Shoe Store, Sports Wear,
Men's Clothing
Average price: Modest
Area: Back Bay
Address: 333 Newbury St
Boston, MA 02115
Phone: (617) 369-7091

#176
Equinox
Category: Gym, Sports Wear
Average price: Exclusive
Area: Financial District
Address: 225 Franklin St
Boston, MA 02110
Phone: (617) 426-2140

#177
Skoah Boston
Category: Skin Care,
Cosmetics, Beauty Supply
Average price: Expensive
Area: South End
Address: 641a Tremont St
Boston, MA 02118
Phone: (857) 350-4930

#178
The Goodwill Store
Category: Thrift Store
Average price: Inexpensive
Area: Allston/Brighton
Address: 965 Commonwealth Ave
Boston, MA 02215
Phone: (617) 254-0112

#179
More Than Words
Category: Bookstore,
Venues, Event Space
Average price: Inexpensive
Area: South End
Address: 242 E Berkeley St
Boston, MA 02118
Phone: (781) 788-0035

#180
ADCO Diamond Corporation
Category: Jewelry
Average price: Expensive
Area: Downtown
Address: 333 Washington St
Boston, MA 02108
Phone: (617) 720-0752

#181
Condom World
Category: Adult
Average price: Modest
Area: Back Bay
Address: 332 Newbury St
Boston, MA 02115
Phone: (617) 267-7233

#182
Ball & Buck
Category: Men's Hair Salon
Average price: Expensive
Area: Back Bay
Address: 144B Newbury St
Boston, MA 02116
Phone: (617) 262-1776

#183
Camper
Category: Shoe Store
Average price: Expensive
Area: Back Bay
Address: 139 Newbury St
Boston, MA 02116
Phone: (617) 267-4554

#184
Nanette Lepore
Category: Women's Clothing,
Accessories, Swimwear
Average price: Expensive
Area: Back Bay
Address: 119 Newbury St
Boston, MA 02116
Phone: (617) 421-9200

#185
Fat Tony's
Category: Sports Wear
Average price: Modest
Area: Back Bay
Address: 273 Newbury St
Boston, MA 02116
Phone: (617) 236-4990

#186
Ashmont Cycles
Category: Bikes
Average price: Modest
Area: Dorchester
Address: 551A Talbot Ave
Boston, MA 02124
Phone: (617) 282-6552

#187
European Watch Company
Category: Watches, Watch Repair
Average price: Expensive
Area: Back Bay
Address: 232 Newbury St
Boston, MA 02116
Phone: (617) 262-9798

#188
Bobbles & Lace
Category: Women's Clothing, Jewelry
Average price: Modest
Area: Back Bay
Address: 251 Newbury Street
Boston, MA 02116
Phone: (857) 239-9202

#189
MakerBot
Category: Computers
Average price: Exclusive
Area: Back Bay
Address: 144 Newbury St
Boston, MA 02116
Phone: (617) 307-7828

#190
Old Japan Inc.
Category: Cards, Stationery,
Home Decor, Gift Shop
Average price: Modest
Area: South End
Address: 22-24 Union Park St
Boston, MA 02118
Phone: (617) 357-8800

#191
Aesop
Category: Cosmetics, Beauty Supply
Average price: Expensive
Area: Back Bay
Address: 172 Newbury St
Boston, MA 02116
Phone: (212) 899-3450

#192
Eugene Gallery
Category: Art Gallery
Average price: Expensive
Area: Beacon Hill
Address: 76 Charles St
Boston, MA 02114
Phone: (617) 227-3062

#193
Colonial Trading Co.
Category: Hobby Shop,
Pawn Shop, Jewelry
Average price: Exclusive
Area: Downtown
Address: 102 Tremont St
Boston, MA 02228
Phone: (617) 695-1652

#194
Paul Duggan Co.
Category: Jewelry, Watches
Average price: Exclusive
Area: Downtown
Address: 333 Washington St
Boston, MA 02108
Phone: (617) 742-0221

#195
Skylight Jewelers
Category: Jewelry
Average price: Expensive
Area: Downtown
Address: 44 School St
Boston, MA 02108
Phone: (617) 426-0521

#196
Landry's Bicycles
Category: Bike Rentals, Bikes
Average price: Expensive
Area: Allston/Brighton
Address: 890 Commonwealth Ave
Boston, MA 02215
Phone: (617) 232-0446

#197
Robin's Flower Shop
Category: Florist
Average price: Modest
Area: Downtown
Address: 1 Devonshire Pl
Boston, MA 02109
Phone: (617) 523-4433

#198
Lekker Home
Category: Furniture Store, Home Decor
Average price: Expensive
Area: South End
Address: 1313 Washington St
Boston, MA 02118
Phone: (617) 542-6464

#199
AllSaints
Category: Women's Clothing,
Accessories, Men's Clothing
Average price: Expensive
Area: Back Bay
Address: 122 Newbury Street
Boston, MA 02116
Phone: (617) 517-0894

#200
Gucci
Category: Leather Goods,
Men's Clothing, Women's Clothing
Average price: Exclusive
Area: Back Bay
Address: 800 Boylston Street, TS#101A
Boston, MA 02199
Phone: (617) 247-3000

#201
Johnny Cupcakes
Category: Men's Clothing,
Women's Clothing
Average price: Expensive
Area: Back Bay
Address: 279 Newbury St
Boston, MA 02116
Phone: (617) 375-0100

#202
Optical Shop of Aspen
Category: Eyewear, Opticians
Average price: Expensive
Area: Back Bay
Address: 800 Boylston St, Ste 147
Boston, MA 02199
Phone: (617) 375-7978

#203
Photographic Resource Center
Category: Art Gallery
Average price: Inexpensive
Area: Allston/Brighton
Address: 832 Commonwealth Ave
Boston, MA 02215
Phone: (617) 975-0600

#204
Johnson Paint Company
Category: Hardware Store
Average price: Modest
Area: Back Bay
Address: 355 Newbury St
Boston, MA 02115
Phone: (617) 536-4244

#205
Kenmore Army & Navy Store
Category: Men's Clothing,
Women's Clothing, Discount Store
Average price: Modest
Area: Downtown
Address: 477 Washington St
Boston, MA 02111
Phone: (617) 292-2769

#206
Watch Hospital
Category: Watches, Watch Repair
Average price: Inexpensive
Area: Downtown
Address: 40 Bromfield St
Boston, MA 02108
Phone: (617) 542-8332

#207
Michele Bernard
Category: Florist
Average price: Modest
Area: Back Bay
Address: Newbury St
Boston, MA 02116
Phone: (800) 856-2199

#208
Tangerine Creations
Category: Wedding Planning, Florist
Average price: Expensive
Area: South End
Address: 141 Malden St
Boston, MA 02118
Phone: (617) 202-0299

#209
Ceremony Boston
Category: Bridal
Average price: Expensive
Area: Beacon Hill
Address: 48 Charles St
Boston, MA 02114
Phone: (857) 277-1669

#210
Essex Corner
Category: Home Decor, Flowers, Gifts
Average price: Inexpensive
Area: Chinatown
Address: 50 Essex St
Boston, MA 02111
Phone: (617) 338-8882

#211
John J. Fleming Jewelry
Category: Jewelry
Average price: Modest
Area: Downtown
Address: 387 Washington St
Boston, MA 02108
Phone: (617) 542-7793

#212
Second Time Around
Category: Vintage
Average price: Modest
Area: Back Bay
Address: 176 Newbury St
Boston, MA 02116
Phone: (617) 247-3504

#213
Studio Optics
Category: Eyewear, Opticians
Average price: Modest
Area: Back Bay
Address: 229 Berkeley St
Boston, MA 02116
Phone: (617) 247-0012

#214
Anais Jewelry
Category: Jewelry
Average price: Modest
Area: Downtown
Address: 333 Washington St
Boston, MA 02108
Phone: (857) 991-1103

#215
Platinum Studio by Z.
Category: Jewelry
Average price: Modest
Area: Downtown
Address: 333 Washington St
Boston, MA 02108
Phone: (617) 227-1559

#216
Sousa Jewelers
Category: Jewelry
Average price: Modest
Area: Downtown
Address: 333 Washington St
Boston, MA 02108
Phone: (617) 367-3461

#217
Mouradian Jewelry
Category: Jewelry
Average price: Modest
Area: Downtown
Address: 333 Washington St
Boston, MA 02108
Phone: (617) 248-8610

#218
Alex and Ani
Category: Jewelry
Average price: Modest
Area: Back Bay
Address: 115 Newbury St
Boston, MA 02116
Phone: (617) 421-0777

#219
Williams-Sonoma
Category: Kitchen & Bath
Average price: Expensive
Area: Back Bay
Address: 100 Huntington Ave
Boston, MA 02116
Phone: (617) 262-3080

#220
Cartier
Category: Jewelry
Average price: Exclusive
Area: Back Bay
Address: 40 Newbury St
Boston, MA 02116
Phone: (617) 262-3300

#221
City Sports
Category: Sporting Goods
Average price: Modest
Area: Downtown
Address: 11 Bromfield St
Boston, MA 02108
Phone: (617) 423-2020

#222
Supercuts
Category: Hair Salon,
Cosmetics, Beauty Supply
Average price: Inexpensive
Area: Back Bay
Address: 829 Boylston St
Boston, MA 02116
Phone: (617) 236-0310

#223
Staples
Category: Office Equipment
Average price: Modest
Area: Fenway
Address: 401 Park Dr
Boston, MA 02215
Phone: (617) 638-3292

#224
**Savas Studio Boutique
& Photography Studio**
Category: Women's Clothing,
Makeup Artists, Session Photography
Average price: Inexpensive
Area: North End
Address: 456 Hanover St
Boston, MA 02113
Phone: (617) 728-7775

#225
Madbury Road
Category: Furniture Store
Average price: Modest
Area: Charlestown
Address: 33 Monument Sq
Boston, MA 02129
Phone: (203) 554-2385

#226
Deprisco Diamond Jewelers
Category: Jewelry
Average price: Expensive
Area: Downtown
Address: 333 Washington St
Boston, MA 02108
Phone: (617) 227-3339

#227
Neiman Marcus
Category: Department Store
Average price: Exclusive
Address: 5 Copley Pl
Boston, MA 02116
Phone: (617) 536-3660

#228
J. Crew
Category: Men's Clothing,
Women's Clothing
Average price: Expensive
Area: Back Bay
Address: 100 Huntington Ave
Boston, MA 02116
Phone: (617) 236-5950

#229
Simon Pearce Retail Store
Category: Home Decor, Bridal
Average price: Exclusive
Area: Back Bay
Address: 103 Newbury St
Boston, MA 02116
Phone: (617) 450-8388

#230
Rag & Bone
Category: Men's Clothing,
Women's Clothing
Average price: Expensive
Area: Back Bay
Address: 111 Newbury St
Boston, MA 02116
Phone: (617) 536-6700

#231
Hugo Boss
Category: Men's Clothing
Average price: Expensive
Area: Back Bay
Address: 100 Huntington Avenue
Boston, MA 02116
Phone: (617) 266-7492

#232
ÁDeux: Bespoke Wedding Paper
Category: Cards, Stationery
Average price: Expensive
Area: Charlestown
Address:
Boston, MA 02129
Phone: (617) 398-0542

#233
Koko Jewelry
Category: Jewelry
Average price: Modest
Area: Back Bay
Address: 800 Boylston St
Boston, MA 02199
Phone: (617) 236-8289

#234
Diamond Barr Jewelers
Category: Jewelry
Average price: Modest
Area: Beacon Hill
Address: 333 Washington St
Boston, MA 02108
Phone: (617) 723-8510

#235
Envi
Category: Women's Clothing
Average price: Expensive
Area: Waterfront, Leather District
Address: 134 Beach St
Boston, MA 02111
Phone: (617) 267-3684

#236
East Coast Alpine
Category: Outdoor Gear
Average price: Modest
Area: Allston/Brighton
Address: 860 Commonwealth Ave
Boston, MA 02215
Phone: (617) 232-9800

#237
BCBG
Category: Women's Clothing
Average price: Expensive
Area: Back Bay
Address: 71 Newbury St
Boston, MA 02228
Phone: (617) 536-7182

#238
Guitar Center
Category: Musical Instruments
Average price: Modest
Area: Fenway
Address: 1255 Boylston St
Boston, MA 02215
Phone: (617) 247-1389

#239
Max Studio
Category: Women's Clothing
Average price: Expensive
Area: Back Bay
Address: 100 Huntington Ave
Boston, MA 02116
Phone: (617) 236-1154

#240
Benetton For Men
Category: Men's Clothing
Average price: Expensive
Area: Back Bay
Address: 100 Huntington Ave
Boston, MA 02116
Phone: (617) 437-7745

#241
Barnes & Noble
Category: Bookstore
Average price: Expensive
Area: Back Bay
Address: 800 Boylston St
Boston, MA 02199
Phone: (617) 247-6959

#242
Microsoft Store
Category: Computers
Average price: Expensive
Area: Back Bay
Address: 800 Boylston St
Boston, MA 02116
Phone: (617) 692-4000

#243
Supercuts
Category: Hair Salon,
Cosmetics, Beauty Supply
Average price: Inexpensive
Area: Allston/Brighton
Address: 1083 Commonwealth Ave
Boston, MA 02215
Phone: (617) 782-5290

#244
Converse Store
Category: Fashion
Average price: Modest
Area: Back Bay
Address: 348 Newbury St
Boston, MA 02113
Phone: (617) 424-5400

#245
Freedman Jewelers
Category: Jewelry
Average price: Modest
Area: Downtown
Address: 333 Washington St
Boston, MA 02108
Phone: (617) 227-4294

#246
Supercuts
Category: Hair Salon,
Cosmetics, Beauty Supply
Average price: Inexpensive
Area: Downtown
Address: 101 Summer St
Boston, MA 02110
Phone: (617) 350-7200

#247
American Apparel
Category: Men's Clothing,
Women's Clothing, Accessories
Average price: Modest
Area: Back Bay
Address: 138 Newbury St
Boston, MA 02116
Phone: (617) 536-4768

#248
Buffalo Exchange
Category: Vintage,
Men's Clothing, Women's Clothing
Average price: Inexpensive
Area: Allston/Brighton
Address: 180 Harvard Ave
Boston, MA 02134
Phone: (617) 779-7901

#249
Water Management
Category: Kitchen & Bath
Average price: Expensive
Area: Back Bay
Address: 228 Commonwealth Ave
Boston, MA 02116
Phone: (800) 249-2299

#250
City Sports
Category: Sporting Goods
Average price: Modest
Area: Allston/Brighton
Address: 1035 Commonwealth Ave
Boston, MA 02215
Phone: (617) 782-5121

#251
Giorgio Armani Boutique
Category: Women's Clothing,
Men's Clothing
Average price: Exclusive
Area: Back Bay
Address: 22 Newbury St
Boston, MA 02116
Phone: (617) 267-3200

#252
The Backbay Framery
Category: Art Gallery, Framing
Average price: Modest
Area: Back Bay
Address: 227 Newbury St
Boston, MA 02116
Phone: (617) 424-1550

#253
Mayan Weavers
Category: Arts, Crafts, Art Gallery
Average price: Modest
Area: Back Bay
Address: 268 Newbury St
Boston, MA 02116
Phone: (617) 262-4342

#254
Sara Campbell
Category: Women's Clothing
Average price: Modest
Area: South End
Address: 44 Plympton St
Boston, MA 02118
Phone: (617) 423-3134

#255
Uncle Pete's
Category: Men's Clothing
Average price: Expensive
Area: Beacon Hill
Address: 119 Charles St
Boston, MA 02114
Phone: (617) 391-0895

#256
Allen Edmonds
Category: Shoe Store
Average price: Expensive
Area: Financial District
Address: 25 State St
Boston, MA 02228
Phone: (617) 557-3131

#257
Giant Cycling World Boston
Category: Bikes, Outdoor Gear
Average price: Modest
Area: Fenway
Address: 11 Kilmarnock St
Boston, MA 02215
Phone: (617) 424-6400

#258
Levi's Newbury
Category: Men's Clothing,
Women's Clothing, Accessories
Average price: Modest
Area: Back Bay
Address: 131 Newbury Street
Boston, MA 02116
Phone: (617) 262-0135

#259
Olympia Flower Store
Category: Florist
Average price: Modest
Area: South End
Address: 1745 Washington St
Boston, MA 02118
Phone: (617) 262-2000

#260
Brodney Antiques & Jewelry
Category: Jewelry, Antiques
Average price: Exclusive
Area: Back Bay
Address: 145 Newbury St
Boston, MA 02116
Phone: (617) 536-0500

#261
Vineyard Vines
Category: Fashion
Average price: Expensive
Area: Back Bay
Address: 800 Boylston Street
Boston, MA 02199
Phone: (617) 927-0490

#262
Longchamp Boston
Category: Leather Goods,
Department Store
Average price: Expensive
Area: Back Bay
Address: 139 Newbury St
Boston, MA 02116
Phone: (617) 425-0740

#263
Ann Taylor
Category: Women's Clothing
Average price: Expensive
Area: Back Bay
Address: 800 Boylston St Ste 27
Boston, MA 02199
Phone: (617) 421-9097

#264
Mohr & McPherson
Category: Home Decor,
Furniture Store
Average price: Expensive
Area: South End
Address: 460 Harrison Ave
Boston, MA 02118
Phone: (617) 210-7900

#265
Nordstrom Rack
Category: Department Store
Average price: Modest
Area: Back Bay
Address: 497 Boylston St
Boston, MA 02116
Phone: (857) 300-2300

#266
AT&T
Category: Mobile Phones
Average price: Modest
Area: Downtown
Address: 371 Washington Street
Boston, MA 02108
Phone: (617) 357-6107

#267
Clarks of England Concept Shop
Category: Shoe Store
Average price: Expensive
Area: Waterfront
Address: 200 State St
Boston, MA 02109
Phone: (617) 261-2320

#268
Eastern Bakers Supply Co Inc
Category: Specialty Food, Kitchen & Bath
Average price: Inexpensive
Area: North End
Address: 145 N Washington St
Boston, MA 02114
Phone: (617) 742-0228

#269
Lacoste
Category: Women's Clothing,
Men's Clothing, Shoe Store
Average price: Expensive
Area: Back Bay
Address: 800 Boylston Street
Boston, MA 02116
Phone: (617) 437-1081

#270
Sikara & Co
Category: Jewelry
Average price: Modest
Area: Back Bay
Address: 250 Newbury St
Boston, MA 02116
Phone: (617) 236-7770

#271
Back Bay Florist
Category: Florist
Average price: Modest
Area: Back Bay
Address: 90 Massachusetts Ave
Boston, MA 02115
Phone: (617) 236-0101

#272
LF
Category: Women's Clothing
Average price: Expensive
Area: Back Bay
Address: 353 Newbury St
Boston, MA 02115
Phone: (617) 236-1213

#273
Warren Electric & Hardware Supply
Category: Hardware Store
Average price: Modest
Area: South End
Address: 470 Tremont St
Boston, MA 02116
Phone: (617) 426-7525

#274
True Religion Brand Jeans
Category: Men's Clothing, Women's
Clothing, Children's Clothing
Average price: Expensive
Area: Back Bay
Address: 119 Newbury St
Boston, MA 02116
Phone: (617) 585-3050

#275
Benefit Cosmetics & Brow Bar
Category: Hair Removal, Cosmetics,
Beauty Supply, Makeup Artists
Average price: Expensive
Area: Back Bay
Address: 156 Newbury St
Boston, MA 02116
Phone: (617) 830-7110

#276
L'Occitane en Provence
Category: Cosmetics, Beauty Supply
Average price: Modest
Area: Back Bay
Address: 800 Boylston St
Boston, MA 02116
Phone: (617) 536-4289

#277
Urban Outfitters
Category: Women's Clothing,
Men's Clothing, Home Decor
Average price: Modest
Area: Back Bay
Address: 361 Newbury Street
Boston, MA 02115
Phone: (617) 236-0088

#278
Jimmy Choo
Category: Shoe Store
Average price: Exclusive
Area: South Boston
Address: 100 Huntington Avenue
Boston, MA 02118
Phone: (617) 927-9570

#279
Brookstone
Category: Home & Garden,
Gift Shop, Electronics
Average price: Expensive
Area: Back Bay
Address: 100 Huntington Ave
Boston, MA 02116
Phone: (617) 267-4308

#280
Express
Category: Fashion
Average price: Modest
Area: Back Bay
Address: 800 Boylston St
Boston, MA 02199
Phone: (617) 587-0906

#281
Allen Edmonds
Category: Shoe Store
Average price: Expensive
Area: Back Bay
Address: 36 Newbury St
Boston, MA 02116
Phone: (617) 247-3363

#282
Amazing Video Store
Category: Video Game Rental, Adult
Average price: Modest
Area: Chinatown
Address: 57 Stuart St
Boston, MA 02116
Phone: (617) 338-1252

#283
Free People
Category: Fashion
Average price: Expensive
Area: Back Bay
Address: 800 Boylston St
Boston, MA 02199
Phone: (617) 450-4902

#284
Yale Appliance & Lighting
Category: Appliances & Repair,
Lighting Fixtures, Equipment
Average price: Modest
Area: Dorchester
Address: 296 Freeport St
Boston, MA 02122
Phone: (617) 825-9253

#285
CVS/Pharmacy
Category: Drugstore
Average price: Inexpensive
Area: Back Bay
Address: 587 Boylston St
Boston, MA 02116
Phone: (617) 437-8414

#286
T-Mobile
Category: Mobile Phones
Average price: Exclusive
Area: Back Bay
Address: 118 Newbury Street
Boston, MA 02116
Phone: (617) 425-5300

#287
Q Optical
Category: Eyewear, Opticians
Average price: Expensive
Area: Back Bay
Address: 287 Newbury St
Boston, MA 02115
Phone: (617) 424-9292

#288
The Ruby Door
Category: Jewelry
Average price: Expensive
Area: Downtown
Address: 15 Charles Street
Boston, MA 02228
Phone: (617) 720-2001

#289
DVF
Category: Women's Clothing
Average price: Expensive
Area: Back Bay
Address: 73 Newbury St
Boston, MA 02116
Phone: (617) 247-7300

#290
Elie Tahari
Category: Women's Clothing,
Men's Clothing
Average price: Expensive
Area: Back Bay
Address: 100 Huntington Ave
Boston, MA 02116
Phone: (617) 536-5851

#291
Scott James
Category: Men's Clothing
Average price: Expensive
Area: Back Bay
Address: 160 Newbury St
Boston, MA 02116
Phone: (617) 247-9700

#292
DTR Modern Gallery
Category: Art Gallery
Average price: Exclusive
Area: Back Bay
Address: 167 Newbury St
Boston, MA 02116
Phone: (617) 424-9700

#293
No Rest For Bridget
Category: Women's Clothing,
Accessories, Shoe Store
Average price: Modest
Area: Back Bay
Address: 220 Newbury St
Boston, MA 02116
Phone: (617) 236-5650

#294
Himalayas Collection
Category: Women's Clothing,
Antiques, Personal Shopping
Average price: Modest
Area: Back Bay
Address: 230 Newbury St
Boston, MA 02116
Phone: (617) 536-6666

#295
Hefez & Sons Jewelers
Category: Jewelry
Average price: Expensive
Area: Downtown
Address: 387 Washington St
Boston, MA 02108
Phone: (617) 451-2797

#296
Vision Care 2000
Category: Eyewear, Opticians
Average price: Modest
Area: Financial District
Address: 48 High St
Boston, MA 02110
Phone: (617) 542-2020

#297
Green Street Vault
Category: Shoe Store, Men's Clothing
Average price: Modest
Area: South Boston
Address: 90 L St
Boston, MA 02127
Phone: (617) 396-4792

#298
Laura Preshong Gallery
Category: Jewelry, Bridal, Leather Goods
Average price: Modest
Area: South End
Address: 558 Tremont St
Boston, MA 02118
Phone: (617) 236-7660

#299
Shecky's Girls Night Out
Category: Shopping
Average price: Modest
Area: Back Bay
Address: 539 Tremont St
Boston, MA 02116
Phone: (617) 426-5000

#300
Bella Bridesmaid
Category: Bridal
Average price: Modest
Area: Back Bay
Address: 85 Newbury St
Boston, MA 02116
Phone: (617) 424-7231

#301
Winston Flowers
Category: Florist
Average price: Expensive
Area: Financial District
Address: 176 Federal St
Boston, MA 02228
Phone: (617) 541-1100

#302
New England Eye
Category: Eyewear, Opticians
Average price: Expensive
Area: Allston/Brighton
Address: 930 Commonwealth Ave
Boston, MA 02215
Phone: (617) 262-2020

#303
Dorfman Jewelers
Category: Jewelry
Average price: Exclusive
Area: Back Bay
Address: 24 Newbury St
Boston, MA 02116
Phone: (617) 536-2022

#304
Polo Ralph Lauren
Category: Men's Clothing,
Women's Clothing
Average price: Expensive
Area: Back Bay
Address: 93 Newbury St
Boston, MA 02116
Phone: (617) 424-1124

#305
Blick Art Materials
Category: Art Supplies, Hobby Shop
Average price: Modest
Area: Fenway
Address: 401 Park Dr
Boston, MA 02215
Phone: (617) 247-3322

#306
Ann Taylor Loft
Category: Women's Clothing
Average price: Modest
Area: Back Bay
Address: 800 Boylston St Ste 11
Boston, MA 02199
Phone: (617) 262-9411

#307
The Dr. Martens Store
Category: Shoe Store
Average price: Expensive
Area: Back Bay
Address: 201 Newbury
Boston, MA 02116
Phone: (617) 585-1460

#308
MarsHall
Category: Department Store
Average price: Inexpensive
Area: Downtown
Address: 350 Washington St
Boston, MA 02108
Phone: (617) 338-6205

#309
Ten Thousand Villages
Category: Jewelry, Home Decor
Average price: Modest
Area: Downtown
Address: 252 Washington St
Boston, MA 02108
Phone: (617) 372-8743

#310
Second Time Around
Category: Vintage,
Women's Clothing
Average price: Modest
Area: Beacon Hill
Address: 82 Charles St
Boston, MA 02114
Phone: (617) 227-0049

#311
Lunarik Fashions
Category: Jewelry, Accessories
Average price: Expensive
Area: Back Bay
Address: 279 Newbury St
Boston, MA 02116
Phone: (617) 236-4400

#312
Gary Drug Co.
Category: Drugstore
Average price: Expensive
Area: Beacon Hill
Address: 59 Charles St
Boston, MA 02114
Phone: (617) 227-0023

#313
West Elm
Category: Furniture Store
Average price: Expensive
Area: Fenway
Address: 160 Brookline Ave
Boston, MA 02215
Phone: (617) 450-9500

#314
MarsHall
Category: Department Store
Average price: Modest
Area: Fenway
Address: 126 Brookline Ave
Boston, MA 02215
Phone: (617) 369-5080

#315
Wet Seal
Category: Women's Clothing
Average price: Inexpensive
Area: Downtown
Address: 7 Winter St
Boston, MA 02108
Phone: (617) 695-3590

#316
Barbour
Category: Fashion
Average price: Expensive
Area: Back Bay
Address: 134 Newbury Street
Boston, MA 02116
Phone: (617) 375-7829

#317
The Art of Shaving
Category: Cosmetics, Beauty Supply
Average price: Modest
Area: Back Bay
Address: 139B Newbury St
Boston, MA 02116
Phone: (857) 239-7261

#318
Best Buy
Category: Electronics, Mobile Phones
Average price: Modest
Area: Fenway
Address: 401 Park Dr
Boston, MA 02215
Phone: (617) 424-7900

#319
CVS/Pharmacy
Category: Photography Store
Average price: Modest
Area: Beacon Hill
Address: 155 Charles Street
Boston, MA 02114
Phone: (617) 523-1028

#320
South Bay Center
Category: Shopping Center
Average price: Modest
Area: Dorchester
Address: 8 Allstate Rd
Boston, MA 02125
Phone: (617) 369-6600

#321
Tiffany & Co
Category: Jewelry
Average price: Expensive
Area: Back Bay
Address: 100 Huntington Ave
Boston, MA 02116
Phone: (617) 353-0222

#322
Stitch Boutique
Category: Arts, Crafts, Hobby Shop
Average price: Modest
Area: Back Bay
Address: 231 Berkeley St
Boston, MA 02116
Phone: (617) 236-4633

#323
CVS/Pharmacy
Category: Drugstore
Average price: Inexpensive
Area: Downtown
Address: 2 Center Plz
Boston, MA 02108
Phone: (617) 523-1105

#324
Ann Taylor Loft
Category: Accessories
Average price: Modest
Area: Waterfront
Address: 200 State Street
Boston, MA 02109
Phone: (617) 737-7840

#325
CVS/Pharmacy
Category: Drugstore,
Photography Store&Service
Average price: Modest
Area: Back Bay
Address: 240 Newbury St.
Boston, MA 02116
Phone: (617) 236-4007

#326
Second Time Around
Category: Vintage
Average price: Modest
Area: Back Bay
Address: 324 Newbury St.
Boston, MA 02115
Phone: (617) 236-2028

#327
Macy's
Category: Department Store,
Men's Clothing, Women's Clothing
Average price: Modest
Area: Downtown
Address: 450 Washington St
Boston, MA 02111
Phone: (617) 357-3000

#328
The Picture Store
Category: Art Gallery, Framing
Average price: Exclusive
Area: South End
Address: 65 Berkeley St
Boston, MA 02116
Phone: (617) 426-5144

#329
Montage
Category: Furniture Store
Average price: Exclusive
Area: Back Bay
Address: 75 Arlington St
Boston, MA 02116
Phone: (617) 451-9400

#330
Maricruz Hairstyles
Category: Hair Salon, Bridal
Average price: Modest
Area: Back Bay
Address: 50 Arlington St
Boston, MA 02116
Phone: (617) 938-7523

#331
The Vintage Garden
Category: Nursery, Gardening
Average price: Modest
Area: South End
Address: 59 Dartmouth St
Boston, MA 02116
Phone: (857) 265-3689

#332
Sur La Table
Category: Kitchen & Bath, Appliances
Average price: Modest
Area: Back Bay
Address: 100 Huntinton Ave
Boston, MA 02116
Phone: (617) 236-4525

#333
AIC Boston Center
Category: Venues, Event Space,
Music Venues, Art Gallery
Average price: Modest
Area: Back Bay
Address: 38 Newbury St
Boston, MA 02116
Phone: (617) 266-0080

#334
Akris Boutique
Category: Women's Clothing
Average price: Expensive
Area: Back Bay
Address: 16 Newbury St
Boston, MA 02116
Phone: (617) 536-6225

#335
Twelve Chairs
Category: Home Decor
Average price: Expensive
Area: South End
Address: 581 Tremont St
Boston, MA 02118
Phone: (617) 701-3496

#336
James Perse
Category: Women's Clothing,
Men's Clothing
Average price: Expensive
Area: Back Bay
Address: 17 Arlington St
Boston, MA 02116
Phone: (617) 369-4570

#337
Boston Piano Tuner
Category: Musical Instruments
Average price: Modest
Area: Back Bay
Address: 10 Huntington Ave
Boston, MA 02116
Phone: (978) 869-9650

#338
Faxon Green
Category: Florist
Average price: Expensive
Area: Back Bay
Address: 125 Newbury St
Boston, MA 02116
Phone: (617) 697-9868

#339
Niche Urban Garden Supply
Category: Nursery, Gardening
Average price: Modest
Area: South End
Address: 619 Tremont St
Boston, MA 02118
Phone: (857) 753-4294

#340
Boston Marathon Finish Line
Category: Sports Wear
Average price: Inexpensive
Area: Back Bay
Address: 671 Boylston St
Boston, MA 02116
Phone: (617) 267-4774

#341
OKW
Category: Women's Clothing
Average price: Expensive
Area: South End
Address: 631 A Tremont St
Boston, MA 02118
Phone: (617) 266-4114

#342
Gallery Kayafas
Category: Art Gallery
Average price: Expensive
Area: South End
Address: 450 Harrison Ave
Boston, MA 02118
Phone: (617) 482-0411

#343
Samsøn
Category: Art Gallery
Average price: Expensive
Area: South End
Address: 450 Harrison Ave
Boston, MA 02118
Phone: (617) 357-7177

#344
Boston Guitar Repair Center
Category: Musical Instruments,
Performing Arts, Specialty School
Average price: Modest
Area: South End
Address: 131 W Concord St
Boston, MA 02118
Phone: (857) 207-2248

#345
Table & Tulip
Category: Florist
Average price: Modest
Area: South End
Address: 461 Shawmut Ave
Boston, MA 02118
Phone: (617) 262-3100

#346
The Frye Company
Category: Leather Goods, Shoe Store
Average price: Expensive
Area: Back Bay
Address: 284 Newbury St
Boston, MA 02115
Phone: (617) 247-3793

#347
Keezing Kreations
Category: Jewelry
Average price: Modest
Area: Beacon Hill
Address: 333 Washington St
Boston, MA 02108
Phone: (617) 650-9934

#348
Felicia's Cosmetics
Category: Skin Care,
Cosmetics, Beauty Supply
Average price: Expensive
Area: Back Bay
Address: 314 Newbury St
Boston, MA 02115
Phone: (617) 927-4433

#349
KM Hudson
Category: Lingerie
Average price: Expensive
Area: Beacon Hill
Address: 125 Charles St
Boston, MA 02114
Phone: (617) 624-9620

#350
Forever Diamond
Category: Jewelry, Bridal, Gold Buyers
Average price: Modest
Area: Downtown
Address: 333 Washington St
Boston, MA 02108
Phone: (617) 523-1060

#351
Rader's Engraving
Category: Jewelry
Average price: Inexpensive
Area: Downtown
Address: 333 Washington Street
Boston, MA 02108
Phone: (617) 227-2921

#352
The Perfume Corner
Category: Cosmetics, Beauty Supply
Average price: Modest
Area: Downtown
Address: 8 Milk St
Boston, MA 02108
Phone: (617) 542-7638

#353
Mona Lisa Jewelers
Category: Jewelry, Bridal
Average price: Modest
Area: Beacon Hill
Address: 333 Washington St
Boston, MA 02108
Phone: (617) 723-4199

#354
Sol Optics
Category: Eyewear, Opticians
Average price: Expensive
Area: North End
Address: 329 Hanover St
Boston, MA 02113
Phone: (617) 523-3005

#355
Newbury Yarns
Category: Knitting Supplies
Average price: Modest
Area: Back Bay
Address: 166 Newbury St
Boston, MA 02116
Phone: (617) 572-3733

#356
Zara
Category: Women's Clothing,
Men's Clothing
Average price: Modest
Area: Back Bay
Address: 214 Newbury St
Boston, MA 02116
Phone: (617) 236-1414

#357
Louis Vuitton
Category: Fashion, Luggage
Average price: Exclusive
Area: Back Bay
Address: Copley Pl
Boston, MA 02116
Phone: (617) 437-6519

#358
Boston Flower Market
Category: Florist
Average price: Modest
Area: South End
Address: 591 Albany St
Boston, MA 02118
Phone: (617) 357-7009

#359
Hudson News
Category: Newspapers, Magazines,
Convenience Store
Average price: Expensive
Area: East Boston
Address: 1 Harborside Dr
Boston, MA 02128
Phone: (201) 939-5050

#360
Rue La La
Category: Outlet Store
Average price: Modest
Area: South Boston
Address: 20 Channel Ctr
Boston, MA 02210
Phone: (888) 992-5252

#361
Levenger
Category: Office Equipment,
Luggage, Accessories
Average price: Expensive
Area: Back Bay
Address: 800 Boylston St
Boston, MA 02199
Phone: (617) 536-3434

#362
Life is Good
Category: Men's Clothing,
Women's Clothing
Average price: Expensive
Address: 285 Newbury Street
Boston, MA 02115
Phone: (617) 262-5068

#363
The Blues Jean Bar
Category: Women's Clothing,
Men's Clothing
Average price: Expensive
Area: Back Bay
Address: 85 Newbury St
Boston, MA 02116
Phone: (857) 350-4683

#364
Party City
Category: Party Supplies
Average price: Modest
Area: Back Bay
Address: 356 Boylston St
Boston, MA 02116
Phone: (617) 450-0355

#365
La Perla
Category: Lingerie
Average price: Exclusive
Area: Back Bay
Address: 250 Boylston St
Boston, MA 02116
Phone: (617) 423-5709

#366
In the Pink
Category: Women's Clothing
Average price: Expensive
Area: Back Bay
Address: 133 Newbury St
Boston, MA 02116
Phone: (617) 536-6423

#367
**The Greater Boston Bigfoot
Research Institute**
Category: Shopping
Average price: Inexpensive
Area: Egleston Square
Address: 3035 Washington St
Boston, MA 02119
Phone: (617) 442-5400

#368
Banana Republic Men's
Category: Men's Clothing
Average price: Expensive
Area: Back Bay
Address: 4 Copley Pl
Boston, MA 02116
Phone: (617) 867-0400

#369
De Scenza Diamonds
Category: Jewelry, Watches
Average price: Expensive
Area: Downtown
Address: 387 Washington St
Boston, MA 02108
Phone: (617) 542-7975

#370
Diseño
Category: Home Decor,
Furniture Store
Average price: Modest
Area: South End
Address: 460B Harrison St
Boston, MA 02228
Phone: (617) 423-2008

#371
CVS/Pharmacy
Category: Drugstore
Average price: Modest
Area: North End
Address: 218 Hanover St
Boston, MA 02113
Phone: (617) 720-2688

#372
Johnston & Murphy Shop
Category: Shoe Store
Average price: Modest
Area: Back Bay
Address: 800 Boylston Street
Boston, MA 02199
Phone: (617) 437-0255

#373
American Apparel
Category: Men's Clothing,
Women's Clothing
Average price: Modest
Area: Back Bay
Address: 330 Newbury St
Boston, MA 02115
Phone: (617) 236-1636

#374
Bouvier Jewelers
Category: Jewelry
Average price: Modest
Area: Downtown
Address: 333 Washington St
Boston, MA 02108
Phone: (617) 742-7080

#375
L'elite Bridal Boutique
Category: Bridal, Sewing, Alterations
Average price: Expensive
Area: Back Bay
Address: 14 Newbury St
Boston, MA 02116
Phone: (617) 424-1010

#376
Gracie Finn
Category: Home Decor
Average price: Modest
Area: South End
Address: 18 Union Park St
Boston, MA 02118
Phone: (617) 357-0321

#377
Sunglass Hut International
Category: Eyewear, Opticians
Average price: Expensive
Area: Back Bay
Address: 182 Newbury Street
Boston, MA 02116
Phone: (617) 437-1050

#378
Scoop NYC
Category: Women's Clothing,
Men's Clothing, Accessories
Average price: Expensive
Area: Back Bay
Address: 177 Newbury St
Boston, MA 02116
Phone: (617) 874-4400

#379
Olympia Sports
Category: Sporting Goods
Average price: Modest
Area: Back Bay
Address: 800 Boylston Street
Boston, MA 02199
Phone: (617) 424-6499

#380
Cibeline
Category: Women's Clothing
Average price: Expensive
Area: Beacon Hill
Address: 120 Charles St
Boston, MA 02114
Phone: (617) 742-0244

#381
Salvatore Ferragamo
Category: Shoe Store,
Men's Clothing, Women's Clothing
Average price: Exclusive
Area: Downtown
Address: 100 Huntington Ave
Boston, MA 02228
Phone: (617) 859-4924

#382
CVS/Pharmacy
Category: Drugstore
Average price: Inexpensive
Area: South Boston
Address: 425 W Broadway
Boston, MA 02127
Phone: (617) 269-7656

#383
The Walking Company
Category: Shoe Store
Average price: Modest
Area: Back Bay
Address: 100 Huntington Ave.
Boston, MA 02116
Phone: (617) 536-9255

#384
Aldo Accessories
Category: Fashion
Average price: Modest
Area: Back Bay
Address: 184 Newbury St
Boston, MA 02116
Phone: (617) 266-2189

#385
Jack Wills
Category: Women's Clothing,
Men's Clothing
Average price: Expensive
Area: Back Bay
Address: 179 Newbury St
Boston, MA 02116
Phone: (857) 753-4524

#386
Lou Lou
Category: Jewelry, Fashion
Average price: Modest
Area: Back Bay
Address: 222A Newbury St
Boston, MA 02115
Phone: (857) 265-3952

#387
Louis Barry Florist
Category: Florist
Average price: Modest
Area: Back Bay
Address: Prudential Ctr
Boston, MA 02199
Phone: (617) 437-1058

#388
Goodwill Store
Category: Thrift Store
Average price: Inexpensive
Area: South Boston
Address: 470 W Broadway
Boston, MA 02127
Phone: (617) 307-6367

#389
Swarovski Gallery Store
Category: Jewelry, Home Decor
Average price: Expensive
Area: Back Bay
Address: 800 Boylston St
Boston, MA 02199
Phone: (617) 578-0705

#390
Tourneau
Category: Jewelry, Watches,
Watch Repair
Average price: Expensive
Area: Back Bay
Address: 100 Huntington Ave
Boston, MA 02116
Phone: (617) 267-8463

#391
J McLaughlin
Category: Men's Clothing,
Women's Clothing, Sports Wear
Average price: Expensive
Area: Beacon Hill
Address: 34 Charles St
Boston, MA 02114
Phone: (617) 228-4195

#392
Orpheus Performing Arts
Category: Music & DVDs
Average price: Modest
Area: Fenway
Address: 362 Commonwealth Ave
Boston, MA 02115
Phone: (617) 247-7200

#393
Men's Wearhouse
Category: Men's Clothing, Formal Wear
Average price: Modest
Area: Back Bay
Address: 406 Boylston Street
Boston, MA 02116
Phone: (617) 266-9296

#394
Tello's
Category: Fashion
Average price: Inexpensive
Area: Downtown
Address: 449 Washington St
Boston, MA 02111
Phone: (617) 482-0058

#395
Barmakian Jewelers
Category: Jewelry
Average price: Expensive
Area: Downtown
Address: 333 Washington St, Ste 720
Boston, MA 02108
Phone: (617) 227-3724

#396
Papyrus
Category: Cards, Stationery
Average price: Expensive
Area: Downtown
Address: 70 Franklin St Ste 1
Boston, MA 02110
Phone: (617) 330-5172

#397
Staples the Office Superstore
Category: Office Equipment
Average price: Modest
Area: Downtown
Address: 25 Court St
Boston, MA 02108
Phone: (617) 367-1747

#398
CVS/Pharmacy
Category: Drugstore
Average price: Inexpensive
Area: Fenway
Address: 1249 Boylston St
Boston, MA 02215
Phone: (617) 262-1354

#399
Guess
Category: Women's Clothing
Average price: Expensive
Area: Back Bay
Address: 80 Newbury St
Boston, MA 02116
Phone: (617) 236-4147

#400
Juicy Couture
Category: Fashion
Average price: Expensive
Area: Back Bay
Address: 12 Newbury St
Boston, MA 02228
Phone: (617) 236-5514

#401
Blooms to Doors
Category: Florist
Average price: Expensive
Area: Allston/Brighton
Address: 119 Braintree St
Boston, MA 02134
Phone: (617) 202-0299

#402
Rainbow Apparel
Category: Fashion
Average price: Inexpensive
Area: Downtown
Address: 13 Winter St
Boston, MA 02111
Phone: (617) 451-6460

#403
Bil Mooney-McCoy
Category: Musical Instruments
Average price: Modest
Area: Dorchester
Address:
Boston, MA 02124
Phone: (617) 202-8327

#404
HomeGoods
Category: Home Decor
Average price: Modest
Area: Allston/Brighton
Address: 60 Everett St
Boston, MA 02135
Phone: (617) 787-4999

#405
Oro Gold
Category: Cosmetics, Beauty Supply,
Accessories, Skin Care
Average price: Exclusive
Area: Back Bay
Address: 100 Huntington Ave
Boston, MA 02116
Phone: (877) 554-1777

#406
CVS/Pharmacy
Category: Photography Store
Average price: Modest
Area: Downtown
Address: 55 Summer St
Boston, MA 02110
Phone: (617) 542-3153

#407
Gamestop
Category: Video Game Rental
Average price: Modest
Area: Downtown
Address: 40 Winter St
Boston, MA 02108
Phone: (617) 210-7923

#408
Cambridge Eye Doctors
Category: Eyewear, Opticians
Average price: Modest
Area: Financial District
Address: 100 State St
Boston, MA 02109
Phone: (617) 742-2076

#409
Lucky Brand Jeans
Category: Fashion
Average price: Expensive
Area: Back Bay
Address: 100 Huntington Ave
Boston, MA 02116
Phone: (617) 247-1289

#410
Brooks Brothers
Category: Men's Clothing
Average price: Expensive
Area: Financial District
Address: 75 State St
Boston, MA 02109
Phone: (617) 261-9990

#411
Victoria's Secret
Category: Lingerie, Accessories
Average price: Expensive
Area: Back Bay
Address: 100 Huntington Ave
Boston, MA 02116
Phone: (617) 266-7505

#412
Gamestop
Category: Video Game Rental,
Electronics
Average price: Modest
Area: Back Bay
Address: 800 Boylston St
Boston, MA 02199
Phone: (617) 236-4432

#413
Apple Store
Category: Electronics, Computers
Average price: Expensive
Area: Back Bay
Address: 815 Boylston St
Boston, MA 02116
Phone: (617) 385-9400

#414
Papyrus
Category: Cards, Stationery
Average price: Expensive
Area: Back Bay
Address: 800 Boylston St
Boston, MA 02199
Phone: (617) 262-6520

#415
Solstice
Category: Eyewear, Opticians
Average price: Expensive
Area: Back Bay
Address: 168 Newbury St
Boston, MA 02228
Phone: (617) 450-4922

#416
Otaku
Average price: Modest
Area: Chinatown
Address: 44 Kneeland St
Boston, MA 02111
Phone: (617) 556-8258

#417
Gazelle
Category: Electronics
Average price: Expensive
Area: Waterfront, South Boston
Address: 25 Thomson Pl
Boston, MA 02210
Phone: (800) 800-8000

#418
Tibet Emporium
Category: Jewelry, Women's Clothing
Average price: Modest
Area: Beacon Hill
Address: 103 Charles St
Boston, MA 02114
Phone: (617) 723-8035

#419
Fossil
Category: Men's Clothing,
Women's Clothing
Average price: Modest
Area: Back Bay
Address: 359 Newbury St
Boston, MA 02115
Phone: (617) 236-2068

#420
Forever 21
Category: Fashion
Average price: Inexpensive
Area: Back Bay
Address: 343 Newbury St
Boston, MA 02115
Phone: (617) 262-0212

#421
Spectacle
Category: Eyewear, Opticians
Average price: Modest
Area: South End
Address: 544 Tremont St
Boston, MA 02116
Phone: (617) 542-9600

#422
Sleepy's Boston
Category: Mattresses
Average price: Expensive
Area: Back Bay
Address: 811 Boylston Street
Boston, MA 02116
Phone: (617) 456-1694

#423
Mitchell Gold + Bob Williams
Category: Furniture Store
Average price: Modest
Area: Back Bay
Address: 142 Berkeley Street
Boston, MA 02116
Phone: (617) 266-0075

#424
Ana Hernandez
Category: Bridal
Average price: Expensive
Area: Back Bay
Address: 165 Newbury St
Boston, MA 02116
Phone: (617) 536-2500

#425
CVS/Pharmacy
Category: Drugstore
Average price: Inexpensive
Area: South End
Address: 400 Tremont St
Boston, MA 02116
Phone: (617) 542-2107

#426
Life In Boston
Category: Outlet Store
Average price: Expensive
Area: Back Bay
Address: 800 Boylston St
Boston, MA 02199
Phone: (617) 572-3614

#427
NRO
Category: Men's Clothing,
Women's Clothing
Average price: Expensive
Area: Beacon Hill
Address: 126 Charles St
Boston, MA 02114
Phone: (617) 742-0089

#428
CVS/Pharmacy
Category: Drugstore,
Cosmetics, Beauty Supply
Average price: Modest
Area: Downtown
Address: 333 Washington St
Boston, MA 02108
Phone: (617) 742-0783

#429
Rite Aid
Category: Drugstore
Average price: Inexpensive
Area: Downtown
Address: 100 Cambridge St
Boston, MA 02114
Phone: (617) 367-4704

#430
The Boston Gardener
Category: Nursery, Gardening
Average price: Modest
Area: Dudley Square
Address: 2131 Washington St
Boston, MA 02119
Phone: (617) 606-7065

#431
IL DECOR
Category: Interior Design,
Furniture Store, Home Decor
Average price: Exclusive
Area: Back Bay
Address: 10 St James Ave
Boston, MA 02116
Phone: (617) 580-3443

#432
Anne Fontaine
Category: Women's Clothing
Average price: Expensive
Area: Back Bay
Address: 318 Boylston St
Boston, MA 02116
Phone: (617) 423-5565

#433
Alan Bilzerian
Category: Men's Clothing,
Women's Clothing
Average price: Exclusive
Area: Back Bay
Address: 34 Newbury St
Boston, MA 02116
Phone: (617) 536-1001

#434
Alexis Bittar
Category: Jewelry
Average price: Modest
Area: Back Bay
Address: 130 Newbury St
Boston, MA 02116
Phone: (617) 236-0505

#435
FastFrame
Category: Framing
Average price: Expensive
Area: South End
Address: 105 E Berkeley St
Boston, MA 02118
Phone: (617) 542-0908

#436
Carroll & Sons Gallery
Category: Art Gallery
Average price: Expensive
Area: South End
Address: 450 Harrison Ave
Boston, MA 02118
Phone: (617) 482-2477

#437
Timberland
Category: Women's Clothing,
Men's Clothing
Average price: Expensive
Area: Back Bay
Address: 201 Newbury St
Boston, MA 02116
Phone: (617) 247-1478

#438
Tobey Grey
Category: Women's Clothing,
Men's Clothing
Average price: Expensive
Area: Back Bay
Address: 218 Newbury St
Boston, MA 02116
Phone: (857) 233-4809

#439
Tobias & Battite
Category: Health & Medical
Average price: Modest
Area: Downtown
Address: 16 Temple Pl
Boston, MA 02111
Phone: (617) 426-2226

#440
Noa Jewelry,
Fine Handcrafts & Gifts
Category: Jewelry, Art Gallery,
Home Decor
Average price: Expensive
Area: Beacon Hill
Address: 88 Charles St
Boston, MA 02114
Phone: (857) 233-4912

#441
Athleta
Category: Women's Clothing
Average price: Expensive
Area: Back Bay
Address: 92 Newbury St
Boston, MA 02116
Phone: (617) 587-9830

#442
Robert Marc Sale Shop
Category: Eyewear, Opticians
Average price: Expensive
Area: Back Bay
Address: 35 Newbury St
Boston, MA 02116
Phone: (617) 450-4900

#443
VIRA Boutique
Category: Women's Clothing
Average price: Expensive
Area: Beacon Hill
Address: 107 Charles St
Boston, MA 02114
Phone: (617) 367-0305

#444
MinuteMan Coin & Jewelry
Category: Jewelry
Average price: Inexpensive
Area: Downtown
Address: 29 Bromfield St
Boston, MA 02108
Phone: (617) 778-0409

#445
Vessel South End
Category: Home Decor
Average price: Modest
Area: South End
Address: 652 Tremont St
Boston, MA 02118
Phone: (617) 425-5292

#446
Kung Fu Video & Dvd
Category: Video Game Rental
Average price: Inexpensive
Area: Downtown
Address: 365 Washington St
Boston, MA 02108
Phone: (617) 451-3336

#447
Dubin Jewelers
Category: Jewelry
Average price: Inexpensive
Area: Downtown
Address: 333 Washington St
Boston, MA 02108
Phone: (617) 742-3132

#448
Boston Diamond Exchange
Category: Jewelry
Average price: Modest
Area: Downtown
Address: 333 Washington St
Boston, MA 02108
Phone: (617) 475-3028

#449
Frette
Category: Home Decor, Fashion
Average price: Exclusive
Area: Back Bay
Address: 776B Boylston St
Boston, MA 02199
Phone: (617) 267-0500

#450
Bally
Category: Shoe Store
Average price: Exclusive
Area: Beacon Hill
Address: 100 Huntington Ave
Boston, MA 02108
Phone: (617) 437-1910

#451
Ararat Jewelry
Category: Jewelry
Average price: Modest
Area: Downtown
Address: 333 Washington St
Boston, MA 02108
Phone: (617) 523-0918

#452
The Borrowed Dress
Category: Women's Clothing, Bridal
Average price: Modest
Area: North End
Address: 256 Hanover St
Boston, MA 02113
Phone: (617) 286-2088

#453
Clarks
Category: Shoe Store
Average price: Expensive
Area: North End
Address: 200 State St
Boston, MA 02109
Phone: (617) 261-2320

#454
Men's Wearhouse
Category: Men's Clothing
Average price: Modest
Area: Downtown
Address: 481 Washington St.
Boston, MA 02111
Phone: (617) 423-5030

#455
Sedurre
Category: Lingerie, Accessories,
Women's Clothing
Average price: Modest
Area: North End
Address: 28 1/2 Prince St
Boston, MA 02113
Phone: (617) 720-4400

#456
Design Within Reach
Category: Furniture Store,
Home Decor
Average price: Expensive
Area: South End
Address: 519 Tremont St
Boston, MA 02116
Phone: (617) 451-7801

#457
Prem La
Category: Arts, Crafts
Average price: Modest
Area: Back Bay
Address: 209 Newbury St
Boston, MA 02096
Phone: (617) 536-5614

#458
Murphy's Jewelry
Category: Jewelry
Average price: Modest
Area: South Boston
Address: 619 E Broadway
Boston, MA 02127
Phone: (617) 268-0033

#459
Headquarters Hair Salon
Category: Hair Salon,
Cosmetics, Beauty Supply
Average price: Modest
Address: 545 E Broadway
Boston, MA 02127
Phone: (617) 269-0085

#460
Backstage
Hardware & Theatre Supply
Category: Hardware Store
Average price: Modest
Address: 21 Drydock Ave
Boston, MA 02210
Phone: (617) 330-1422

#461
Restoration Hardware
Category: Furniture Store
Average price: Expensive
Area: Back Bay
Address: 234 Berkley St
Boston, MA 02116
Phone: (851) 239-7202

#462
Victoria's Secret
Category: Lingerie
Average price: Modest
Area: Back Bay
Address: 82 Newbury St
Boston, MA 02116
Phone: (617) 424-7290

#463
Nahas Shoes
Category: Shoe Store
Average price: Expensive
Area: North End
Address: 285 Hanover St
Boston, MA 02113
Phone: (617) 523-6520

#464
Cohen's Fashion Optical
Category: Eyewear, Opticians
Average price: Expensive
Area: Downtown
Address: 328 Washington St
Boston, MA 02108
Phone: (617) 542-9221

#465
Garage Sale Boston
Category: Furniture Store, Home Decor
Average price: Modest
Area: South End
Address: 55 Waltham St
Boston, MA 02118
Phone: (617) 482-7044

#466
Soodee
Category: Women's Clothing
Average price: Expensive
Area: Back Bay
Address: 170 Newbury St
Boston, MA 02116
Phone: (617) 266-7888

#467
Niketown
Category: Shoe Store
Average price: Expensive
Area: Back Bay
Address: 200 Newbury St
Boston, MA 02116
Phone: (617) 267-3400

#468
Stuart Weitzman
Category: Shoe Store
Average price: Expensive
Area: Back Bay
Address: 100 Huntington Ave
Boston, MA 02116
Phone: (617) 266-8699

#469
Color Copy Center Boston
Category: Printing Service
Photography Store&Service
Average price: Inexpensive
Area: Back Bay
Address: 31 St. James Ave
Boston, MA 02116
Phone: (617) 391-0030

#470
Lucky 2 Strokes
Category: Motorcycle Gear,
Motorcycle Dealers
Average price: Modest
Area: Allston/Brighton
Address: 12 Penniman Rd
Boston, MA 02134
Phone: (617) 586-7996

#471
Boston Appliance Company
Category: Appliances
Average price: Modest
Area: South Boston
Address: 840 Summer St
Boston, MA 02127
Phone: (617) 268-7500

#472
Gap
Category: Men's Clothing,
Women's Clothing, Children's Clothing
Average price: Modest
Area: Back Bay
Address: 100 Huntington Ave
Boston, MA 02116
Phone: (617) 247-1754

#473
Verizon Wireless
Category: Mobile Phones, Electronics,
Internet Service Providers
Average price: Modest
Area: Back Bay
Address: 745 Boylston St Ste 107
Boston, MA 02116
Phone: (617) 266-9000

#474
Staples
Category: Office Equipment
Average price: Expensive
Area: Back Bay
Address: 899 Boylston St
Boston, MA 02115
Phone: (617) 262-0310

#475
My Wig World
Category: Wigs
Average price: Expensive
Area: Downtown
Address: 27 Temple Pl
Boston, MA 02111
Phone: (617) 542-5511

#476
Audio Concepts
Category: Home Theatre Installation,
Electronics, Lighting Fixtures, Equipment
Average price: Exclusive
Area: Allston/Brighton
Address: 870 Commonwealth Ave
Boston, MA 02215
Phone: (617) 734-1800

#477
Vera Wang Boston
Category: Sewing, Alterations, Bridal
Average price: Exclusive
Area: Back Bay
Address: 73 Newbury St
Boston, MA 02116
Phone: (617) 424-1060

#478
Jos A Bank
Category: Men's Clothing
Average price: Modest
Area: Back Bay
Address: 399 Boylston Street
Boston, MA 02116
Phone: (617) 536-5050

#479
The Tannery
Category: Shoe Store, Men's Clothing,
Women's Clothing
Average price: Expensive
Area: Back Bay
Address: 711 Boylston St
Boston, MA 02215
Phone: (617) 267-5500

#480
Payless Shoe Source
Category: Shoe Store
Average price: Modest
Area: Beacon Hill
Address: 367 Washington Street
Boston, MA 02108
Phone: (617) 451-1871

#481
Crocs
Category: Shoe Store
Average price: Modest
Area: Waterfront
Address: 200 State St
Boston, MA 02109
Phone: (617) 478-4953

#482
Fenway: South End
Category: Internal Medicine,
Counseling & Mental Health, Drugstore
Average price: Modest
Area: Back Bay
Address: 142 Berkeley St
Boston, MA 02116
Phone: (617) 247-7555

#483
AT&T
Category: Mobile Phones
Average price: Expensive
Area: Back Bay
Address: 647 Boylston St
Boston, MA 02116
Phone: (617) 369-9000

#484
Basics Carpet and Furniture
Category: Furniture Store
Average price: Inexpensive
Area: Allston/Brighton
Address: 1119 Commonwealth Ave
Boston, MA 02215
Phone: (617) 254-2250

#485
**Ermenegildo Zegna
Boston Boutique**
Category: Men's Clothing
Average price: Exclusive
Area: Back Bay
Address: 39 Newbury St
Boston, MA 02116
Phone: (617) 424-9300

#486
Ann Taylor
Category: Women's Clothing
Average price: Modest
Area: Back Bay
Address: 18 Newbury St
Boston, MA 02228
Phone: (617) 262-0763

#487
Mila Lilu
Category: Toy Store, Baby Gear &
Furniture, Children's Clothing
Average price: Modest
Address: 100 Huntington Ave
Boston, MA 02116
Phone: (617) 266-6452

#488
Empire Loan
Category: Jewelry, Pawn Shop
Average price: Expensive
Area: South End
Address: 1130 Washington St
Boston, MA 02118
Phone: (617) 423-9366

#489
Ted Baker London
Category: Women's Clothing,
Men's Clothing
Average price: Expensive
Area: Back Bay
Address: 201 Newbury St
Boston, MA 02116
Phone: (617) 450-8339

#490
The Designers Leather Clothiers
Category: Leather Goods,
Sewing, Alterations
Average price: Expensive
Area: Beacon Hill
Address: 106 Charles St
Boston, MA 02114
Phone: (617) 720-3967

#491
Winston Flowers
Category: Florist
Average price: Expensive
Area: Back Bay
Address: 131 Newbury St
Boston, MA 02116
Phone: (617) 541-1100

#492
Indique Virgin Hair Extensions
Category: Cosmetics, Beauty Supply
Average price: Expensive
Area: South Boston
Address: 380 Dorchester Ave
Boston, MA 02127
Phone: (617) 379-1280

#493
Sprint
Category: Mobile Phones
Average price: Expensive
Area: Back Bay
Address: 422 Boylston St
Boston, MA 02116
Phone: (617) 747-1300

#494
Brooks Brothers
Category: Men's Clothing,
Women's Clothing
Average price: Expensive
Area: Back Bay
Address: 46 Newbury St
Boston, MA 02116
Phone: (617) 267-2600

#495
Ensemble
Category: Vintage
Average price: Expensive
Area: North End
Address: 62 Salem St
Boston, MA 02113
Phone: (617) 455-8711

#496
Dollar City
Category: Shopping
Average price: Inexpensive
Area: South Boston
Address: 443 W Broadway
Boston, MA 02127
Phone: (617) 268-5388

#497
Arden B
Category: Women's Clothing
Average price: Expensive
Area: Back Bay
Address: 800 Boylston St
Boston, MA 02199
Phone: (617) 236-0834

#498
Paperchase
Category: Cards, Stationery
Average price: Expensive
Area: Back Bay
Address: 172 Newbury St
Boston, MA 02116
Phone: (617) 236-2221

#499
MiniLuxe
Category: Nail Salon,
Cosmetics, Beauty Supply
Average price: Expensive
Area: West Roxbury
Address: 639 Veterans of Foreign Wars
Pkwy, Boston, MA 02467
Phone: (617) 327-1777

#500
Boston HeadShots
Category: Photography Store, Service
Average price: Modest
Area: Waterfront, Leather District
Address: 210 Lincoln St
Boston, MA 02111
Phone: (617) 963-0158

TOP 500 RESTAURANTS

Most Recommended by Locals & Trevelers
Ranking (from #1 to #500)

#1
Piperi Mediterranean Grill
Cuisines: Mediterranean
Average price: Under $10
Area: Downtown
Address: One Beacon St
Boston, MA 02108
Phone: (617) 227-7471

#2
Dave's Fresh Pasta
Cuisines: Specialty Food, Sandwiches
Average price: $11-30
Area: Davis Square
Address: 81 Holland St
Somerville, MA 02144
Phone: (617) 623-0867

#3
Roast Beast
Cuisines: Sandwiches, Burgers
Average price: Under $10
Area: Allston/Brighton
Address: 1080 Commonwealth Ave
Boston, MA 02215
Phone: (617) 877-8690

#4
Neptune Oyster
Cuisines: Seafood
Average price: $31-60
Area: North End
Address: 63 Salem St
Boston, MA 02113
Phone: (617) 742-3474

#5
Casa Razdora
Cuisines: Italian, Pizza
Average price: Under $10
Area: Financial District
Address: 115 Water St
Boston, MA 02109
Phone: (617) 338-6700

#6
FoMu
Cuisines: Café, Vegan
Average price: Under $10
Area: Allston/Brighton
Address: 481 Cambridge St
Allston, MA 02134
Phone: (617) 903-3276

#7
Zo
Cuisines: Greek
Average price: Under $10
Area: Downtown
Address: 3 Center Plz
Boston, MA 02108
Phone: (617) 901-6017

#8
Menton
Cuisines: French, Italian
Average price: Above $61
Area: Waterfront, South Boston
Address: 354 Congress St
Boston, MA 02210
Phone: (617) 737-0099

#9
Hungry Mother
Cuisines: Southern
Average price: $31-60
Area: Kendall Square/MIT
Address: 233 Cardinal Medeiros Ave
Cambridge, MA 02141
Phone: (617) 499-0090

#10
Giacomo's Ristorante
Cuisines: American
Average price: $11-30
Area: North End
Address: 355 Hanover St
Boston, MA 02113
Phone: (617) 523-9026

#11
Oleana Restaurant
Cuisines: Mediterranean
Average price: $31-60
Area: Inman Square
Address: 134 Hampshire St
Cambridge, MA 02139
Phone: (617) 661-0505

#12
Guru The Caterer
Cuisines: Indian, Caterer
Average price: Under $10
Area: Teele Square
Address: 1297 Broadway
Somerville, MA 02144
Phone: (617) 718-0078

#13
Ten Tables
Cuisines: American
Average price: $31-60
Area: Jamaica Plain
Address: 597 Centre St
Jamaica Plain, MA 02130
Phone: (617) 524-8810

#14
Sam LaGrassa's
Cuisines: Sandwiches
Average price: $11-30
Area: Downtown
Address: 44 Province St
Boston, MA 02108
Phone: (617) 357-6861

#15
L'Espalier
Cuisines: French
Average price: Above $61
Area: Back Bay
Address: 774 Boylston St
Boston, MA 02199
Phone: (617) 262-3023

#16
Blunch
Cuisines: Breakfast & Brunch,
Coffee & Tea
Average price: Under $10
Area: South End
Address: 59 E Springfield St
Boston, MA 02118
Phone: (617) 247-8100

#17
El Pelón Taquería
Cuisines: Mexican, Gluten-Free
Average price: Under $10
Area: Fenway
Address: 92 Peterborough St
Boston, MA 02215
Phone: (617) 262-9090

#18
Taqueria Jalisco
Cuisines: Mexican
Average price: Under $10
Area: East Boston
Address: 291 Bennington St
Boston, MA 02128
Phone: (617) 567-6367

#19
Toro
Cuisines: Tapas Bar
Average price: $31-60
Area: South End
Address: 1704 Washington St
Boston, MA 02118
Phone: (617) 536-4300

#20
Ariana
Cuisines: Afghan, Vegetarian
Average price: $11-30
Area: Allston/Brighton
Address: 129 Brighton Ave
Boston, MA 02134
Phone: (617) 208-8072

#21
Cocobeet
Cuisines: Juice Bar
Average price: $31-60
Area: Downtown
Address: 100 City Hall Plz
Boston, MA 02108
Phone: (857) 263-8598

#22
Salts Restaurant
Cuisines: French, American
Average price: Above $61
Area: Kendall Square/MIT
Address: 798 Main St
Cambridge, MA 02139
Phone: (617) 876-8444

#23
Life Alive
Cuisines: Vegetarian, Vegan
Average price: $11-30
Area: Central Square
Address: 765 Mass Ave
Cambridge, MA 02139
Phone: (617) 354-5433

#24
Galleria Umberto
Cuisines: Pizza, Salad
Average price: Under $10
Area: North End
Address: 289 Hanover St
Boston, MA 02113
Phone: (617) 227-5709

#25
The Capital Grille
Cuisines: Steakhouse, American
Average price: Above $61
Area: Back Bay
Address: 900 Boylston St
Boston, MA 02115
Phone: (617) 262-8900

#26
Blackstrap BBQ
Cuisines: Barbeque
Average price: $11-30
Area: Winthrop
Address: 47 Woodside Ave
Winthrop, MA 02152
Phone: (617) 207-1783

#27
Avana Sushi
Cuisines: Japanese, Sushi Bar
Average price: Under $10
Area: Chinatown
Address: 42 Beach St
Boston, MA 02111
Phone: (617) 818-7782

#28
Rino's Place
Cuisines: Italian
Average price: $11-30
Area: East Boston
Address: 258 Saratoga St
Boston, MA 02128
Phone: (617) 567-7412

#29
Al's State Street Cafe
Cuisines: Sandwiches, Salad
Average price: Under $10
Area: Financial District
Address: 110 State St
Boston, MA 02109
Phone: (617) 720-5555

#30
Atlantic Fish Company
Cuisines: Seafood, Pub
Average price: $31-60
Area: Back Bay
Address: 761 Boylston St
Boston, MA 02116
Phone: (617) 267-4000

#31
Café Mami
Cuisines: Japanese
Average price: Under $10
Area: Porter Square
Address: 1815 Massachusetts Ave
Cambridge, MA 02140
Phone: (617) 547-9130

#32
No. 9 Park
Cuisines: French, Italian
Average price: Above $61
Area: Downtown
Address: 9 Park St
Boston, MA 02108
Phone: (617) 742-9991

#33
Mistral Restaurant
Cuisines: American
Average price: Above $61
Area: Back Bay
Address: 223 Columbus Ave
Boston, MA 02116
Phone: (617) 867-9300

#34
Banh Mi Ngon
Cuisines: Vietnamese, Sandwiches
Average price: Under $10
Area: West Roxbury Center
Address: 1759 Centre St.
Boston, MA 02132
Phone: (617) 325-0946

#35
Drink
Cuisines: Lounge, American
Average price: $31-60
Area: Waterfront, South Boston
Address: 348 Congress St
Boston, MA 02228
Phone: (617) 695-1806

#36
KO Catering and Pies
Cuisines: Breakfast & Brunch
Average price: Under $10
Area: South Boston
Address: 87 A St
Boston, MA 02127
Phone: (617) 269-4500

#37
Mrs. Jones
Cuisines: Soul Food, Southern
Average price: Under $10
Area: Dorchester
Address: 2255 Dorchester Ave
Dorchester, MA 02124
Phone: (617) 696-0180

#38
Amsterdam Falafelshop
Cuisines: Middle Eastern, Falafel
Average price: Under $10
Area: Davis Square
Address: 248 Elm St
Somerville, MA 02144
Phone: (617) 764-3334

#39
Regina Pizzeria
Cuisines: Pizza, Italian
Average price: $11-30
Area: North End
Address: 11 1/2 Thacher St
Boston, MA 02113
Phone: (617) 227-0765

#40
The Druid
Cuisines: Pub, Irish
Average price: $11-30
Area: Inman Square
Address: 1357 Cambridge St
Cambridge, MA 02139
Phone: (617) 497-0965

#41
The Haven
Cuisines: Gastropub, Scottish
Average price: $11-30
Area: Jamaica Plain
Address: 2 Perkins St
Jamaica Plain, MA 02130
Phone: (617) 524-2836

#42
Deep Ellum
Cuisines: Pub, American
Average price: $11-30
Area: Allston/Brighton
Address: 477 Cambridge St
Allston, MA 02134
Phone: (617) 787-2337

#43
Canto 6
Cuisines: Bakery, Coffee & Tea
Average price: Under $10
Area: Jamaica Plain
Address: 3346 Washington St
Jamaica Plain, MA 02130
Phone: (617) 983-8688

#44
The Helmand
Cuisines: Afghan
Average price: $11-30
Area: East Cambridge
Address: 143 1st St
Cambridge, MA 02142
Phone: (617) 492-4646

#45
Falafel King
Cuisines: Falafel
Average price: Under $10
Area: Beacon Hill
Address: 48 Winter St
Boston, MA 02108
Phone: (617) 338-8355

#46
Flour Bakery + Café Central Square
Cuisines: Coffee & Tea, Bakery
Average price: $11-30
Area: Kendall Square/MIT
Address: 190 Massachusetts Ave
Cambridge, MA 02139
Phone: (617) 225-2525

#47
Asta
Cuisines: American
Average price: Above $61
Area: Back Bay
Address: 47 Massachusetts Ave
Boston, MA 02115
Phone: (617) 585-9575

#48
Giulia
Cuisines: Italian
Average price: $31-60
Area: Porter Square
Address: 1682 Massachusetts Ave
Cambridge, MA 02138
Phone: (617) 441-2800

#49
The Shawarma Place
Cuisines: Fast Food, Middle Eastern
Average price: Under $10
Area: Davis Square
Address: 201 Elm St
Somerville, MA 02144
Phone: (617) 666-9000

#50
Cafe Polonia
Cuisines: Polish, Austrian
Average price: $11-30
Area: South Boston
Address: 611 Dorchester Ave
Boston, MA 02127
Phone: (617) 269-0110

#51
Carlo's Cucina Italiana
Cuisines: Italian
Average price: $11-30
Area: Allston/Brighton
Address: 131 Brighton Ave
Allston, MA 02134
Phone: (617) 254-9759

#52
Punjab Palace
Cuisines: Indian
Average price: $11-30
Area: Allston/Brighton
Address: 109 Brighton Ave
Allston, MA 02134
Phone: (617) 254-1500

#53
Shabu-Zen
Cuisines: Japanese, Chinese
Average price: $11-30
Area: Chinatown
Address: 16 Tyler St
Boston, MA 02111
Phone: (617) 292-8828

#54
Cutty's
Cuisines: Coffee & Tea, Sandwiches
Average price: Under $10
Area: Brookline Village
Address: 284 Washington St
Brookline, MA 02445
Phone: (617) 505-1844

#55
East Side Bar & Grille
Cuisines: Italian
Average price: $11-30
Area: East Cambridge
Address: 561 Cambridge St
Cambridge, MA 02141
Phone: (617) 661-3278

#56
Fish Market Sushi Bar
Cuisines: Sushi Bar, Japanese
Average price: $11-30
Area: Allston/Brighton
Address: 170 Brighton Ave
Allston, MA 02134
Phone: (617) 783-1268

#57
Deuxave
Cuisines: American
Average price: Above $61
Area: Back Bay
Address: 371 Commonwealth Ave
Boston, MA 02115
Phone: (617) 517-5915

#58
Ernesto's
Cuisines: Pizza, Desserts
Average price: Under $10
Area: North End
Address: 69 Salem St
Boston, MA 02113
Phone: (617) 523-1373

#59
**D'Amelios Off the Boat Italian
& Seafood Restaurant**
Cuisines: Seafood, Italian
Average price: $11-30
Area: East Boston
Address: 26 Porter St East
Boston, MA 02128
Phone: (617) 561-8800

#60
Cuchi Cuchi
Cuisines: Tapas
Average price: $31-60
Area: Kendall Square/MIT
Address: 795 Main St
Cambridge, MA 02139
Phone: (617) 864-2929

#61
Sorellina
Cuisines: Italian
Average price: Above $61
Area: Back Bay
Address: 1 Huntington Ave
Boston, MA 02116
Phone: (617) 412-4600

#62
Café Luna
Cuisines: Coffee & Tea, Sandwiches
Average price: $11-30
Area: Central Square
Address: 403 Massachusetts Ave
Cambridge, MA 02139
Phone: (617) 576-3400

#63
Toraya
Cuisines: Sushi Bar, Japanese
Average price: $11-30
Area: Arlington Center
Address: 890 Massachusetts Ave
Arlington, MA 02476
Phone: (781) 641-7477

#64
James Hook & Co
Cuisines: Seafood
Average price: $11-30
Area: Waterfront, South Boston
Address: 440 Atlantic Ave
Boston, MA 02111
Phone: (617) 423-5501

#65
Garlic 'n Lemons
Cuisines: Middle Eastern, Mediterranean
Average price: Under $10
Area: Allston/Brighton
Address: 133 Harvard Ave
Allston, MA 02134
Phone: (617) 783-8100

#66
Pomodoro
Cuisines: Italian
Average price: $31-60
Area: North End
Address: 319 Hanover St
Boston, MA 02113
Phone: (617) 367-4348

#67
Navy Yard Bistro & Wine Bar
Cuisines: Wine Bar, American
Average price: $31-60
Area: Charlestown
Address: 6th St
Charlestown, MA 02129
Phone: (617) 242-0036

#68
The Daily Catch
Cuisines: Italian, Seafood
Average price: $11-30
Area: North End
Address: 323 Hanover St
Boston, MA 02113
Phone: (617) 523-8567

#69
Cafe Hemshin
Cuisines: Café, Turkish
Average price: Under $10
Area: Downtown
Address: 8 City Hall Ave
Boston, MA 02108
Phone: (617) 227-0505

#70
Pinocchios Pizza & Subs
Cuisines: Pizza, Salad
Average price: Under $10
Area: Harvard Square
Address: 74 Winthrop St
Cambridge, MA 02138
Phone: (617) 876-4897

#71
The Five Seventy Market
Cuisines: Juice Bar
Average price: $11-30
Area: South End
Address: 570 Tremont St
Boston, MA 02118
Phone: (857) 362-7525

#72
In House Café
Cuisines: Coffee & Tea, Café
Average price: Under $10
Area: Allston/Brighton
Address: 194 Harvard Ave
Allston, MA 02134
Phone: (617) 686-3350

#73
Santarpio's Pizza
Cuisines: Pizza
Average price: Under $10
Area: East Boston
Address: 111 Chelsea St
Boston, MA 02128
Phone: (617) 567-9871

#74
Armando's Pizza & Subs
Cuisines: Pizza, Sandwiches
Average price: Under $10
Area: Huron Village
Address: 163 Huron Ave
Cambridge, MA 02138
Phone: (617) 354-8275

#75
Hamersley's Bistro
Cuisines: American
Average price: $31-60
Area: South End
Address: 553 Tremont St
Boston, MA 02116
Phone: (617) 423-2700

#76
Mi Pueblito Restaurant
Cuisines: Mexican, Latin American
Average price: $11-30
Area: East Boston
Address: 333 Border St
Boston, MA 02128
Phone: (617) 569-3787

#77
Picco
Cuisines: Pizza, Italian
Average price: $11-30
Area: South End
Address: 513 Tremont St
Boston, MA 02116
Phone: (617) 927-0066

#78
Kaze Shabu Shabu
Cuisines: Japanese
Average price: $11-30
Area: Chinatown
Address: 1 Harrison Ave
Boston, MA 02111
Phone: (617) 338-8283

#79
Greek Corner Restaurant
Cuisines: Greek, Mediterranean
Average price: $11-30
Area: North Cambridge
Address: 2366 Massachusetts Ave
Cambridge, MA 02140
Phone: (617) 661-5655

#80
Orinoco
Cuisines: Latin American
Average price: $11-30
Area: South End
Address: 477 Shawmut Ave
Boston, MA 02118
Phone: (617) 369-7075

#81
Tupelo
Cuisines: Southern, Cajun/Creole
Average price: $11-30
Area: Inman Square
Address: 1193 Cambridge St
Cambridge, MA 02139
Phone: (617) 868-0004

#82
KO Pies at the Shipyard
Cuisines: American
Average price: Under $10
Area: East Boston
Address: 256 Marginal St
Boston, MA 02128
Phone: (617) 418-5234

#83
Root
Cuisines: Vegan, Vegetarian
Average price: $11-30
Area: Allston/Brighton
Address: 487 Cambridge St
Allston, MA 02134
Phone: (617) 208-6091

#84
True Bistro
Cuisines: Vegan, Vegetarian
Average price: $11-30
Area: Teele Square
Address: 1153 Broadway
Somerville, MA 02144
Phone: (617) 627-9000

#85
Trattoria Toscana
Cuisines: Italian
Average price: $11-30
Area: Fenway
Address: 130 Jersey St
Boston, MA 02215
Phone: (617) 247-9508

#86
Swish Shabu
Cuisines: Japanese, Sushi Bar
Average price: $11-30
Area: Fenway
Address: 84 86 Peterborough St
Boston, MA 02215
Phone: (617) 236-0255

#87
Cafe Rossetti's
Cuisines: Italian
Average price: $11-30
Area: Winthrop
Address: 115 Winthrop Shore Dr
Winthrop, MA 02152
Phone: (617) 539-9990

#88
City Girl Café
Cuisines: Italian, Breakfast & Brunch
Average price: $11-30
Area: Inman Square
Address: 204 Hampshire St
Cambridge, MA 02139
Phone: (617) 864-2809

#89
Grotto
Cuisines: Italian
Average price: $31-60
Area: Downtown, Beacon Hill
Address: 37 Bowdoin St
Boston, MA 02114
Phone: (617) 227-3434

#90
Toscano Restaurant
Cuisines: Italian
Average price: $31-60
Area: Beacon Hill
Address: 47 Charles St
Boston, MA 02114
Phone: (617) 723-4090

#91
Fogo de Chao Boston
Cuisines: Brazilian, Steakhouse
Average price: $31-60
Area: Back Bay
Address: 200 Dartmouth Street
Boston, MA 02116
Phone: (617) 585-6300

#92
Taranta Cucina Meridionale
Cuisines: Latin American, Italian
Average price: $31-60
Area: North End
Address: 210 Hanover St
Boston, MA 02113
Phone: (617) 720-0052

#93
Garden at the Cellar
Cuisines: Pub, American
Average price: $11-30
Area: Central Square
Address: 991 Massachusetts Ave
Cambridge, MA 02138
Phone: (617) 475-0045

#94
Mamma Maria
Cuisines: Italian
Average price: $31-60
Area: North End
Address: 3 N Square
Boston, MA 02113
Phone: (617) 523-0077

#95
S & I Thai
Cuisines: Thai
Average price: Under $10
Area: Allston/Brighton
Address: 168 Brighton Ave
Allston, MA 02134
Phone: (617) 254-8488

#96
Delfino Restaurant
Cuisines: Italian
Average price: $11-30
Area: Roslindale Village, Roslindale
Address: 754 South St
Roslindale, MA 02131
Phone: (617) 327-8359

#97
Las Ventas
Cuisines: Spanish, Sandwiches
Average price: Under $10
Area: South End
Address: 700 Harrison Ave
Boston, MA 02118
Phone: (617) 266-0443

#98
Blue Ribbon BBQ
Cuisines: Barbeque
Average price: $11-30
Area: Arlington Center
Address: 908 Massachusetts Ave
Arlington, MA 02476
Phone: (781) 648-7427

#99
Lambert's Rainbow Fruit
Cuisines: Fruits & Veggies, Deli
Average price: Under $10
Area: Dorchester
Address: 777 Morrissey Blvd
Dorchester, MA 02122
Phone: (617) 436-2997

#100
Meridian Food Market
Cuisines: Specialty Food, Sandwiches
Average price: Under $10
Area: East Boston
Address: 121 Meridian St East
Boston, MA 02128
Phone: (617) 567-9725

#101
Union Bar and Grille
Cuisines: American
Average price: $31-60
Area: South End
Address: 1357 Washington St
Boston, MA 02118
Phone: (617) 423-0555

#102
Equal Exchange Café
Cuisines: Coffee & Tea, Sandwiches
Average price: Under $10
Area: North End
Address: 226 Causeway St
Boston, MA 02114
Phone: (617) 372-8777

#103
Al's South Street Cafe
Cuisines: Sandwiches
Average price: Under $10
Area: Waterfront, Leather District
Address: 179 Essex St
Boston, MA 02111
Phone: (617) 330-1002

#104
Sunset Grill & Tap
Cuisines: Bar, American
Average price: $11-30
Area: Allston/Brighton
Address: 130 Brighton Ave
Allston, MA 02134
Phone: (617) 254-1331

#105
Lineage
Cuisines: American
Average price: $31-60
Area: Coolidge Corner
Address: 242 Harvard St
Brookline, MA 02446
Phone: (617) 232-0065

#106
Pauli's
Cuisines: Sandwiches, Caterer
Average price: Under $10
Area: North End
Address: 65 Salem St
Boston, MA 02113
Phone: (857) 284-7064

#107
Court House Seafood Restaurant
Cuisines: Seafood Market, Seafood
Average price: $11-30
Area: East Cambridge
Address: 498 Cambridge St
Cambridge, MA 02141
Phone: (617) 491-1213

#108
East Coast Grill
Cuisines: Barbeque, Seafood
Average price: $11-30
Area: Inman Square
Address: 1271 Cambridge St
Cambridge, MA 02139
Phone: (617) 491-6568

#109
Da Vinci Ristorante
Cuisines: Italian
Average price: $31-60
Area: Back Bay
Address: 162 Columbus Ave
Boston, MA 02116
Phone: (617) 350-0007

#110
Flour Bakery + Café
Cuisines: American, Coffee & Tea
Average price: $11-30
Area: Back Bay
Address: 131 Clarendon St
Boston, MA 02116
Phone: (617) 437-7700

#111
My Diner
Cuisines: Diner, Breakfast & Brunch
Average price: Under $10
Area: South Boston
Address: 98 A St
Boston, MA 02127
Phone: (617) 268-9889

#112
Pho Viet's
Cuisines: Vietnamese
Average price: Under $10
Area: Allston/Brighton
Address: 1095 Commonwealth Ave
Boston, MA 02228
Phone: (617) 562-8828

#113
Billy's Sub Shop
Cuisines: Diner, Sandwiches
Average price: Under $10
Area: South End
Address: 57 Berkeley St
Boston, MA 02116
Phone: (617) 426-1822

#114
Giacomo's
Cuisines: Italian
Average price: $11-30
Area: Back Bay
Address: 431 Columbus Ave
Boston, MA 02116
Phone: (617) 536-5723

#115
Michael's Deli
Cuisines: Deli, Caterer
Average price: Under $10
Area: Coolidge Corner
Address: 256 Harvard St
Brookline, MA 02446
Phone: (617) 738-3354

#116
Veggie Galaxy
Cuisines: Vegetarian, Diner
Average price: $11-30
Area: Central Square
Address: 450 Massachusetts Ave
Cambridge, MA 02139
Phone: (617) 497-1513

#117
Andre's Cafe
Cuisines: American
Average price: Under $10
Area: South End
Address: 811 Harrison Ave
Boston, MA 02118
Phone: (617) 267-9599

#118
Franklin Café
Cuisines: Lounge, American
Average price: $11-30
Area: South End
Address: 278 Shawmut Ave
Boston, MA 02118
Phone: (617) 350-0010

#119
Tres Gatos
Cuisines: Tapas Bar, American
Average price: $11-30
Area: Jamaica Plain
Address: 470 Centre St
Jamaica Plain, MA 02130
Phone: (617) 477-4851

#120
Shojo
Cuisines: Chinese, Asian Fusion
Average price: $11-30
Area: Chinatown
Address: 9A Tyler St
Boston, MA 02111
Phone: (617) 423-7888

#121
OTTO
Cuisines: Pizza
Average price: Under $10
Area: Harvard Square
Address: 1432 Mass Ave
Cambridge, MA 02138
Phone: (617) 499-3352

#122
Brown Sugar Cafe
Cuisines: Thai
Average price: $11-30
Area: Allston/Brighton
Address: 1033 Commonwealth Ave
Boston, MA 02215
Phone: (617) 787-4242

#123
Corner Tavern
Cuisines: Bar, American
Average price: $11-30
Area: Back Bay
Address: 421 Marlborough St
Boston, MA 02115
Phone: (617) 262-5555

#124
Emma's Pizza
Cuisines: Pizza
Average price: $11-30
Area: Kendall Square/MIT
Address: 40 Hampshire St
Cambridge, MA 02139
Phone: (617) 864-8534

#125
Green Street
Cuisines: Lounge, American
Average price: $11-30
Area: Central Square
Address: 280 Green St
Cambridge, MA 02139
Phone: (617) 876-1655

#126
Chacarero
Cuisines: Sandwiches, Salad
Average price: Under $10
Area: Downtown
Address: 101 Arch St
Boston, MA 02108
Phone: (617) 542-0392

#127
Cafe Gigu
Cuisines: Café, Wine Bar
Average price: $11-30
Area: East Boston
Address: 102 Meridian St
Boston, MA 02128
Phone: (617) 561-4448

#128
Flatbread Company
Cuisines: Pizza
Average price: $11-30
Area: Davis Square
Address: 45 Day St
Somerville, MA 02144
Phone: (617) 776-0552

#129
Sullivan's
Cuisines: Fast Food, Burgers
Average price: Under $10
Area: South Boston
Address: 2080 Day Blvd
Boston, MA 02127
Phone: (617) 268-5685

#130
Bom Cafe
Cuisines: Brazilian, Café
Average price: Under $10
Area: Inman Square
Address: 1093 Cambridge St
Cambridge, MA 02139
Phone: (617) 864-0395

#131
Sacco's Bowl Haven
Cuisines: Bowling, Pizza
Average price: $11-30
Area: Davis Square
Address: 45 Day St
Somerville, MA 02144
Phone: (617) 776-0552

#132
Taste of India Shanti
Cuisines: Indian, Bangladeshi
Average price: $11-30
Area: Dorchester
Address: 1111 Dorchester Ave
Dorchester, MA 02125
Phone: (617) 929-3900

#133
Newtowne Grille
Cuisines: Pizza, Pub
Average price: Under $10
Area: Porter Square
Address: 1945 Massachusetts Ave
Cambridge, MA 02140
Phone: (617) 661-0706

#134
Angela's Cafe
Cuisines: Mexican
Average price: $11-30
Area: East Boston
Address: 131 Lexington St
Boston, MA 02128
Phone: (617) 567-4972

#135
Istanbul'lu
Cuisines: Turkish, Wine Bar
Average price: $11-30
Area: Teele Square
Address: 237 Holland St
Somerville, MA 02144
Phone: (617) 440-7387

#136
B & G Oysters
Cuisines: Seafood, Italian
Average price: $31-60
Area: South End
Address: 550 Tremont St
Boston, MA 02116
Phone: (617) 423-0550

#137
Rod Dee Thai 2
Cuisines: Thai
Average price: Under $10
Area: Fenway
Address: 94 Peterborough St
Boston, MA 02215
Phone: (617) 859-0969

#138
PARK Restaurant & Bar
Cuisines: American, Bar
Average price: $11-30
Area: Harvard Square
Address: 59 JFK St
Cambridge, MA 02138
Phone: (617) 491-9851

#139
Marliave
Cuisines: French,
Average price: $31-60
Area: Downtown
Address: 10 Bosworth St
Boston, MA 02108
Phone: (617) 422-0004

#140
Roy's Cold Cuts
Cuisines: Deli, Pizza
Average price: Under $10
Area: East Boston
Address: 198 Marion St
Boston, MA 02128
Phone: (617) 567-9760

#141
Coppa
Cuisines: Italian, Tapas
Average price: $31-60
Area: South End
Address: 253 Shawmut Ave
Boston, MA 02118
Phone: (617) 391-0902

#142
Sportello
Cuisines: Italian
Average price: $31-60
Area: Waterfront, South Boston
Address: 348 Congress St
Boston, MA 02210
Phone: (617) 737-1234

#143
Gaslight Brasserie Du Coin
Cuisines: French
Average price: $11-30
Area: South End
Address: 560 Harrison Ave
Boston, MA 02228
Phone: (617) 422-0224

#144
Ruth's Chris Steak House
Cuisines: Steakhouse, Seafood
Average price: Above $61
Area: Downtown
Address: 45 School St
Boston, MA 02108
Phone: (617) 742-8401

#145
Posto
Cuisines: Italian, Pizza
Average price: $11-30
Area: Davis Square
Address: 187 Elm St
Somerville, MA 02144
Phone: (617) 625-0600

#146
Prezza
Cuisines: Italian
Average price: $31-60
Area: North End
Address: 24 Fleet St
Boston, MA 02113
Phone: (617) 227-1577

#147
Veggie Planet
Cuisines: Vegetarian, Pizza
Average price: Under $10
Area: Harvard Square
Address: 47 Palmer St
Cambridge, MA 02138
Phone: (617) 661-1513

#148
Chicken & Rice Guys
Catering & Food Truck
Cuisines: Chicken Wings, Food Truck
Average price: Under $10
Area: Downtown
Address: 5 Childs Rd, Lexington
Boston, MA 02116
Phone: (617) 903-8538

#149
The Village Kitchen
Cuisines: Italian, Pizza
Average price: Under $10
Area: Huron Village
Address: 359 Huron Ave
Cambridge, MA 02138
Phone: (617) 491-3133

#150
Alden & Harlow
Cuisines: American, Breakfast & Brunch
Average price: $31-60
Area: Harvard Square
Address: 40 Brattle St
Cambridge, MA 02138
Phone: (617) 864-2100

#151
Blue Nile Restaurant
Cuisines: Ethiopian
Average price: $11-30
Area: Jamaica Plain
Address: 389 Centre St
Boston, MA 02130
Phone: (617) 522-6453

#152
Deli-icious
Cuisines: Deli
Average price: Under $10
Area: Davis Square
Address: 20 College Ave
Somerville, MA 02144
Phone: (617) 629-4444

#153
FuGaKyu
Cuisines: Sushi Bar, Japanese
Average price: $31-60
Area: Coolidge Corner
Address: 1280 Beacon St
Brookline, MA 02446
Phone: (617) 734-1268

#154
Russell House Tavern
Cuisines: Gastropub, American
Average price: $11-30
Area: Harvard Square
Address: 14 JFK St
Cambridge, MA 02138
Phone: (617) 500-3055

#155
West Bridge
Cuisines: Bar, American
Average price: $31-60
Area: Kendall Square/MIT
Address: 1 Kendall Sq
Cambridge, MA 02141
Phone: (617) 945-0221

#156
Delux Café
Cuisines: Bar, American
Average price: $11-30
Area: South End
Address: 100 Chandler St
Boston, MA 02116
Phone: (617) 338-5258

#157
Lone Star Taco Bar
Cuisines: Mexican
Average price: $11-30
Area: Allston/Brighton
Address: 477 Cambridge St
Allston, MA 02134
Phone: (617) 782-8226

#158
Za
Cuisines: Pizza, Salad
Average price: $11-30
Area: East Arlington
Address: 138 Massachusetts Ave
Arlington, MA 02474
Phone: (781) 316-2334

#159
PS Gourmet Coffee
Cuisines: Coffee & Tea, Deli
Average price: Under $10
Area: South Boston
Address: 106 Dorchester St
Boston, MA 02127
Phone: (617) 269-4020

#160
Myers & Chang
Cuisines: Asian Fusion, Gluten-Free
Average price: $11-30
Area: South End
Address: 1145 Washington St
Boston, MA 02118
Phone: (617) 542-5200

#161
Oishii Boston
Cuisines: Sushi Bar, Japanese
Average price: Above $61
Area: South End
Address: 1166 Washington St
Boston, MA 02118
Phone: (617) 482-8868

#162
Lizard Lounge
Cuisines: Music Venues, Burgers
Average price: $11-30
Area: Porter Square
Address: 1667 Massachusetts Ave
Cambridge, MA 02138
Phone: (617) 547-0759

#163
All Star Sandwich Bar
Cuisines: Sandwiches
Average price: $11-30
Area: Inman Square
Address: 1245 Cambridge St
Cambridge, MA 02139
Phone: (617) 868-3065

#164
The Plough & Stars
Cuisines: Music Venues, American
Average price: $11-30
Area: Central Square
Address: 912 Massachusetts Ave
Cambridge, MA 02139
Phone: (617) 576-0032

#165
**Fleming's Prime Steakhouse
& Wine Bar**
Cuisines: Wine Bar, Steakhouse
Average price: $31-60
Area: Back Bay
Address: 217 Stuart St
Boston, MA 02116
Phone: (617) 292-0808

#166
Silvertone
Cuisines: Italian, Gastropub
Average price: $11-30
Area: Downtown
Address: 69 Bromfield St
Boston, MA 02108
Phone: (617) 338-7887

#167
Kaju Tofu House
Cuisines: Korean
Average price: $11-30
Area: Allston/Brighton
Address: 58 Harvard Ave
Allston, MA 02134
Phone: (617) 208-8540

#168
2nd Street Cafe
Cuisines: Sandwiches, Café
Average price: Under $10
Area: East Cambridge
Address: 89 2nd St
Cambridge, MA 02141
Phone: (617) 661-1311

#169
Harvard Faculty Club
Cuisines: Venues, Event Space
Average price: Above $61
Area: Harvard Square
Address: 20 Quincy St
Cambridge, MA 02138
Phone: (617) 495-5758

#170
The Salty Pig
Cuisines: American
Average price: $11-30
Area: Back Bay
Address: 130 Dartmouth St
Boston, MA 02116
Phone: (617) 536-6200

#171
Jm Curley
Cuisines: American, Lounge
Average price: $11-30
Area: Downtown
Address: 21 Temple Pl
Boston, MA 02111
Phone: (617) 338-5333

#172
The Squeaky Beaker
Cuisines: Café, Comfort Food
Average price: $11-30
Area: East Cambridge
Address: 675 W Kendall St
Cambridge, MA 02142
Phone: (617) 679-0108

#173
Crema Cafe
Cuisines: Coffee & Tea, Café
Average price: $11-30
Area: Harvard Square
Address: 27 Brattle St
Cambridge, MA 02138
Phone: (617) 876-2700

#174
Aquitaine
Cuisines: French
Average price: $31-60
Area: South End
Address: 569 Tremont St
Boston, MA 02118
Phone: (617) 424-8577

#175
La Siesta
Cuisines: Mexican
Average price: $11-30
Area: Winthrop
Address: 70-74 Woodside Ave
Winthrop, MA 02152
Phone: (617) 846-2300

#176
La Siesta
Cuisines: Mexican
Average price: $11-30
Area: Winthrop
Address: 70-74 Woodside Ave
Winthrop, MA 02152
Phone: (617) 846-2300

#177
Al Dente Restaurant
Cuisines: Italian, Bakery
Average price: $11-30
Area: North End
Address: 109 Salem St
Boston, MA 02113
Phone: (617) 523-0990

#178
Thinking Cup
Cuisines: Coffee & Tea, Sandwiches
Average price: $11-30
Area: North End
Address: 236 Hanover St
Boston, MA 02113
Phone: (857) 233-5277

#179
Mikes City Diner
Cuisines: Diner
Average price: Under $10
Area: South End
Address: 1714 Washington St
Boston, MA 02118
Phone: (617) 267-9393

#180
Hana Sushi
Cuisines: Sushi Bar, Japanese
Average price: $11-30
Area: North Cambridge
Address: 2372 Massachusetts Ave
Cambridge, MA 02140
Phone: (617) 868-2121

#181
Bottega Fiorentina
Cuisines: Italian
Average price: Under $10
Area: Coolidge Corner
Address: 313B Harvard St
Brookline, MA 02446
Phone: (617) 232-2661

#182
Darwin's
Cuisines: Deli, Sandwiches
Average price: Under $10
Area: Harvard Square
Address: 148 Mt Auburn St
Cambridge, MA 02138
Phone: (617) 354-5233

#183
Xinh Xinh
Cuisines: Vietnamese, Chinese
Average price: Under $10
Area: Chinatown
Address: 7 Beach St
Boston, MA 02111
Phone: (617) 422-0501

#184
Karo's BBQ
Cuisines: Food Stand, Street Vendor
Average price: Under $10
Area: Downtown
Address: Summer & Hawley St
Boston, MA 02110
Phone: (857) 244-1174

#185
Zaftigs Delicatessen
Cuisines: Breakfast & Brunch, Deli
Average price: $11-30
Area: Coolidge Corner
Address: 335 Harvard St
Brookline, MA 02446
Phone: (617) 975-0075

#186
Galley Diner
Cuisines: Diner, American
Average price: Under $10
Area: South Boston
Address: 11 P St South
Boston, MA 02127
Phone: (617) 464-1024

#187
Spoke
Cuisines: American, Wine Bar
Average price: $31-60
Area: Davis Square
Address: 89 Holland St
Somerville, MA 02144
Phone: (617) 718-9463

#188
North Street Grille
Cuisines: Breakfast & Brunch, American
Average price: $11-30
Area: North End
Address: 229 North St
Boston, MA 02113
Phone: (617) 720-2010

#189
Theo's Cozy Corner
Cuisines: Breakfast & Brunch, Brazilian
Average price: Under $10
Area: North End
Address: 162 Salem St
Boston, MA 02113
Phone: (617) 241-0202

#190
Ula Café
Cuisines: Coffee & Tea, Sandwiches
Average price: Under $10
Area: Jamaica Plain
Address: 284 Amory St
Jamaica Plain, MA 02130
Phone: (617) 524-7890

#191
Bistro Du Midi
Cuisines: French
Average price: $31-60
Area: Back Bay
Address: 272 Boylston St
Boston, MA 02116
Phone: (617) 426-7878

#192
Anchovies
Cuisines: Italian
Average price: $11-30
Area: South End
Address: 433 Columbus Ave
Boston, MA 02116
Phone: (617) 266-5088

#193
Irashai Sushi and Teriyaki
Cuisines: Japanese, Sushi Bar
Average price: $11-30
Area: Chinatown
Address: 8 Kneeland St
Boston, MA 02111
Phone: (617) 350-6888

#194
Yankee Lobster Fish Market
Cuisines: Seafood Market, Seafood
Average price: $11-30
Area: Waterfront, South Boston
Address: 300 Northern Ave
Boston, MA 02210
Phone: (617) 345-9799

#195
JP Licks
Cuisines: Ice Cream
Average price: Under $10
Area: Harvard Square
Address: 1312 Massachusetts Ave
Cambridge, MA 02138
Phone: (617) 492-1001

#196
Boston Kebab House
Cuisines: Turkish, Mediterranean
Average price: Under $10
Area: Financial District
Address: 7 Liberty Sq
Boston, MA 02109
Phone: (617) 227-6900

#197
Sip Cafe
Cuisines: Sandwiches, Coffee & Tea
Average price: Under $10
Area: Financial District
Address: 0 Post Office Sq
Boston, MA 02109
Phone: (617) 338-3080

#198
Pomodoro
Cuisines: Italian
Average price: $31-60
Area: Brookline Village
Address: 24 Harvard St
Brookline, MA 02445
Phone: (617) 566-4455

#199
The Boathouse
Cuisines: American
Average price: $11-30
Area: Harvard Square
Address: 49 Mt Auburn St
Cambridge, MA 02138
Phone: (617) 349-1650

#200
Rox Diner
Cuisines: Breakfast & Brunch
Average price: $11-30
Area: West Roxbury Center
Address: 1881 Center St
West Roxbury, MA 02132
Phone: (617) 327-1909

#201
Rincon Limeño Restaurant
Cuisines: Latin American, Peruvian
Average price: $11-30
Area: East Boston
Address: 409 Chelsea St East
Boston, MA 02128
Phone: (617) 569-4942

#202
Meritage
Cuisines: American, Seafood
Average price: Above $61
Area: Waterfront
Address: 70 Rowes Wharf
Boston, MA 02110
Phone: (617) 439-3995

#203
Row 34
Cuisines: American, Seafood
Average price: $31-60
Area: Waterfront, South Boston
Address: 383 Congress St
Boston, MA 02210
Phone: (617) 553-5900

#204
Limoncello Ristorante
Cuisines: Italian, Wine Bar
Average price: $31-60
Area: North End
Address: 190 N St
Boston, MA 02127
Phone: (617) 523-4480

#205
Punjab
Cuisines: Indian
Average price: $11-30
Area: Arlington Center
Address: 485 Massachusetts Ave
Arlington, MA 02474
Phone: (781) 643-0943

#206
Alia Ristorante
Cuisines: Italian
Average price: $11-30
Area: Winthrop
Address: 495 Shirley St
Winthrop, MA 02152
Phone: (617) 539-1600

#207
The Breakfast Club
Cuisines: Diner, Breakfast & Brunch
Average price: Under $10
Area: Allston/Brighton
Address: 270 Western Ave
Allston, MA 02134
Phone: (617) 783-1212

#208
Yoma
Cuisines: Burmese
Average price: $11-30
Area: Allston/Brighton
Address: 5 N Beacon St
Allston, MA 02134
Phone: (617) 783-1372

#209
Olecito
Cuisines: Mexican
Average price: Under $10
Area: Inman Square
Address: 12 Springfield St
Cambridge, MA 02139
Phone: (617) 876-1374

#210
Stella
Cuisines: Italian, Café
Average price: $31-60
Area: South End
Address: 1525 Washington St
Boston, MA 02118
Phone: (617) 247-7747

#211
SoWa Open Market
Cuisines: Farmer Market
Average price: $11-30
Area: South End
Address: 460 Harrison Ave
Boston, MA 02118
Phone: (800) 403-8305

#212
The Cellar
Cuisines: American, Bar
Average price: $11-30
Area: Central Square
Address: 991 Massachusetts Ave
Cambridge, MA 02138
Phone: (617) 876-2580

#213
Lincoln Tavern & Restaurant
Cuisines: American, Italian
Average price: $11-30
Area: South Boston
Address: 425 W Broadway
Boston, MA 02127
Phone: (617) 765-8636

#214
Figs
Cuisines: Pizza
Average price: $11-30
Area: Beacon Hill
Address: 42 Charles St
Boston, MA 02114
Phone: (617) 742-3447

#215
Abe & Louie's Steak House
Cuisines: Steakhouse, Breakfast & Brunch
Average price: Above $61
Area: Back Bay
Address: 793 Boylston St
Boston, MA 02116
Phone: (617) 536-6300

#216
New England Soup Factory
Cuisines: American, Soup
Average price: Under $10
Area: Brookline Village
Address: 2-4 Brookline Pl
Brookline, MA 02445
Phone: (617) 739-1899

#217
Sam's
Cuisines: American, Burgers
Average price: $11-30
Area: Waterfront, South Boston
Address: 60 Northern Ave
Boston, MA 02210
Phone: (617) 295-0191

#218
La Voile
Cuisines: French
Average price: $31-60
Area: Back Bay
Address: 261 Newbury St
Boston, MA 02116
Phone: (617) 587-4200

#219
Taiwan Café
Cuisines: Taiwanese, Chinese
Average price: Under $10
Area: Chinatown
Address: 34 Oxford St
Boston, MA 02111
Phone: (617) 426-8181

#220
Panza
Cuisines: Italian
Average price: $11-30
Area: North End
Address: 326 Hanover St
Boston, MA 02113
Phone: (617) 557-9248

#221
Bukowski Tavern
Cuisines: Pub, American
Average price: $11-30
Area: Back Bay
Address: 50 Dalton St
Boston, MA 02115
Phone: (617) 437-9999

#222
Mul's Diner
Cuisines: Diner
Average price: Under $10
Area: South Boston
Address: 75 W Broadway
Boston, MA 02127
Phone: (617) 268-5748

#223
Tatte Bakery & Cafe
Cuisines: Bakery, Café
Average price: $11-30
Area: East Cambridge
Address: 318 3rd St
Mid-Cambridge, MA 02142
Phone: (617) 354-4200

#224
Piattini
Cuisines: Italian
Average price: $11-30
Area: Back Bay
Address: 226 Newbury St
Boston, MA 02116
Phone: (617) 536-2020

#225
Grill 23 & Bar
Cuisines: Steakhouse, Wine Bar
Average price: Above $61
Area: Back Bay
Address: 161 Berkeley St
Boston, MA 02116
Phone: (617) 542-2255

#226
Douzo
Cuisines: Sushi Bar, Japanese
Average price: $31-60
Area: Back Bay
Address: 131 Dartmouth St
Boston, MA 02116
Phone: (617) 859-8886

#227
Mr. Dooley's
Cuisines: Bar, Irish
Average price: $11-30
Area: Financial District
Address: 77 Broad St
Boston, MA 02109
Phone: (617) 338-5656

#228
The Paramount
Cuisines: Breakfast & Brunch
Average price: $11-30
Area: Beacon Hill
Address: 44 Charles St
Boston, MA 02114
Phone: (617) 720-1152

#229
Diesel Cafe
Cuisines: Coffee & Tea, Sandwiches
Average price: Under $10
Area: Davis Square
Address: 257 Elm St
Somerville, MA 02144
Phone: (617) 629-8717

#230
Orinoco
Cuisines: Latin American, Caribbean
Average price: $11-30
Area: Brookline Village
Address: 22 Harvard St
Brookline, MA 02445
Phone: (617) 232-9505

#231
Shawarma King
Cuisines: Middle Eastern
Average price: Under $10
Area: Coolidge Corner
Address: 1383 Beacon St
Brookline, MA 02446
Phone: (617) 731-6035

#232
El Oriental De Cuba
Cuisines: Cuban, Caribbean
Average price: $11-30
Area: Jamaica Plain
Address: 416 Centre St
Jamaica Plain, MA 02130
Phone: (617) 524-6464

#233
The Gallows
Cuisines: American
Average price: $11-30
Area: South End
Address: 1395 Washington St
Boston, MA 02118
Phone: (617) 425-0200

#234
Sarah's Market & Cafe
Cuisines: Grocery, Sandwiches
Average price: Under $10
Area: Huron Village
Address: 200 Concord Ave
Cambridge, MA 02138
Phone: (617) 876-5999

#235
The Similans
Cuisines: Thai,
Average price: $11-30
Area: East Cambridge
Address: 145 1st St
Cambridge, MA 02142
Phone: (617) 491-6999

#236
Via Matta
Cuisines: Italian
Average price: $31-60
Area: Back Bay
Address: 79 Park Plz
Boston, MA 02116
Phone: (617) 422-0008

#237
Shawarma Falafel
Cuisines: Middle Eastern,
Average price: Under $10
Area: Downtown
Address: 26 Province St
Boston, MA 02108
Phone: (857) 265-3017

#238
Andala Coffee House
Cuisines: Coffee & Tea, Middle Eastern
Average price: Under $10
Area: Central Square
Address: 286 Franklin St
Cambridge, MA 02139
Phone: (617) 945-2212

#239
Fornax Bread Company
Cuisines: Bakery, Soup
Average price: Under $10
Area: Roslindale Village, Roslindale
Address: 27 Corinth St
Roslindale, MA 02131
Phone: (617) 325-8852

#240
Area Four
Cuisines: Diner, Breakfast & Brunch
Average price: $11-30
Area: Kendall Square/MIT
Address: 500 Technology Sq
 Cambridge, MA 02139
Phone: (617) 758-4444

#241
Falafel King
Cuisines: Middle Eastern, Falafel
Average price: Under $10
Area: Downtown
Address: 260 Washington St
Boston, MA 02108
Phone: (617) 227-6400

#242
Twin DO-Nuts
Cuisines: Donuts, Breakfast & Brunch
Average price: Under $10
Area: Allston/Brighton
Address: 501 Cambridge St
Allston, MA 02134
Phone: (617) 254-9421

#243
Milano's Delicatessen
Cuisines: Deli, Pizza
Average price: Under $10
Area: East Boston
Address: 978 Saratoga St
Boston, MA 02128
Phone: (617) 567-6718

#244
Shays Pub & Wine Bar
Cuisines: American, Wine Bar
Average price: $11-30
Area: Harvard Square
Address: 58 JFK St
Cambridge, MA 02138
Phone: (617) 864-9161

#245
Bottega di Capri
Cuisines: Specialty Food, Italian
Average price: Under $10
Area: Brookline Village
Address: 41 Harvard St
Brookline, MA 02445
Phone: (617) 738-5333

#246
Metropolis Cafe
Cuisines: Wine Bar, Mediterranean
Average price: $11-30
Area: South End
Address: 584 Tremont St
Boston, MA 02118
Phone: (617) 247-2931

#247
Coda
Cuisines: American, Bar
Average price: $11-30
Area: Back Bay
Address: 329 Columbus Ave
Boston, MA 02116
Phone: (617) 536-2632

#248
Rami's
Cuisines: Middle Eastern, Kosher
Average price: $11-30
Area: Coolidge Corner
Address: 324 Harvard St
Brookline, MA 02446
Phone: (617) 738-3577

#249
Le's Restaurant
Cuisines: Vietnamese
Average price: Under $10
Area: Allston/Brighton
Address: 137 Brighton Ave
Allston, MA 02134
Phone: (617) 783-2340

#250
Mei Sum
Cuisines: Bakery, Sandwiches
Average price: Under $10
Area: Chinatown
Address: 36 Beach St
Boston, MA 02111
Phone: (617) 357-4050

#251
Gyro City
Cuisines: Greek
Average price: Under $10
Area: Fenway
Address: 88 Peterborough St
Boston, MA 02215
Phone: (617) 266-4976

#252
Boston Burger Company
Cuisines: Burgers, Caterer
Average price: $11-30
Area: Davis Square
Address: 37 Davis Sq
Somerville, MA 02144
Phone: (617) 440-7361

#253
The Oceanaire Seafood Room
Cuisines: Seafood
Average price: $31-60
Area: Downtown
Address: 40 Court St
Boston, MA 02108
Phone: (617) 742-2277

#254
Redd's in Rozzie
Cuisines: American
Average price: $11-30
Area: Roslindale Village, Roslindale
Address: 4257 Washington St
Boston, MA 02131
Phone: (617) 325-1000

#255
Trattoria di Monica
Cuisines: Italian
Average price: $31-60
Area: North End
Address: 67 Prince St
Boston, MA 02113
Phone: (617) 720-5472

#256
The Parish Cafe
Cuisines: Sandwiches, Desserts
Average price: $11-30
Area: Back Bay
Address: 361 Boylston St
Boston, MA 02116
Phone: (617) 247-4777

#257
Rangzen Tibetan Place
Cuisines: Food Delivery Service,
Asian Fusion
Average price: $11-30
Area: Central Square
Address: 24 Pearl St
Cambridge, MA 02139
Phone: (617) 354-8881

#258
Banh Mi House
Cuisines: Bubble Tea, Sandwiches
Average price: Under $10
Area: Downtown
Address: 48 Winter St
Boston, MA 02108
Phone: (617) 956-4039

#259
Franklin Southie
Cuisines: American, Lounge
Average price: $11-30
Area: South Boston
Address: 152 Dorchester Ave
Boston, MA 02127
Phone: (617) 269-1003

#260
Masala
Cuisines: Indian, Himalayan/Nepalese
Average price: $11-30
Area: Teele Square
Address: 1127 Broadway
Somerville, MA 02144
Phone: (617) 718-0703

#261
Punjabi Dhaba
Cuisines: Indian
Average price: Under $10
Area: Inman Square
Address: 225 Hampshire St
Cambridge, MA 02139
Phone: (617) 547-8272

#262
The Beehive
Cuisines: Jazz & Blues, American
Average price: $31-60
Area: South End
Address: 541 Tremont St
Boston, MA 02116
Phone: (617) 423-0069

#263
Espresso Love
Cuisines: Coffee & Tea, Sandwiches
Average price: Under $10
Area: Financial District
Address: 33 Broad St
Boston, MA 02109
Phone: (857) 284-7462

#264
Caffé Vittoria
Cuisines: Coffee & Tea, Italian
Average price: Under $10
Area: North End
Address: 296 Hanover St
Boston, MA 02113
Phone: (617) 227-7606

#265
Charlie's Sandwich Shoppe
Cuisines: Sandwiches, Breakfast & Brunch
Average price: Under $10
Area: Back Bay
Address: 429 Columbus Ave
Boston, MA 02116
Phone: (617) 536-7669

#266
Ali's Roti Restaurant
Cuisines: Indian, Caribbean
Average price: Under $10
Area: Mattapan
Address: 1188 Blue Hill Ave
Mattapan, MA 02126
Phone: (617) 298-9850

#267
Allston Diner
Cuisines: Burgers, Diner
Average price: $11-30
Area: Allston/Brighton
Address: 431 Cambridge St
Allston, MA 02134
Phone: (617) 208-8741

#268
New Dong Khanh
Cuisines: Vietnamese, Chinese
Average price: Under $10
Area: Chinatown
Address: 81 Harrison Ave
Boston, MA 02111
Phone: (617) 426-9410

#269
Winsor Dim Sum Café
Cuisines: Dim Sum
Average price: Under $10
Area: Chinatown
Address: 10 Tyler St
Boston, MA 02111
Phone: (617) 338-1688

#270
Dino's Cafe
Cuisines: Italian, Deli
Average price: Under $10
Area: North End
Address: 141 Salem St
Boston, MA 02113
Phone: (617) 227-1991

#271
Ecco Pizzeria
Cuisines: Pizza, Salad
Average price: $11-30
Area: Allston/Brighton
Address: 1147 Commonwealth Ave
Boston, MA 02134
Phone: (617) 903-4324

#272
Sweetgreen
Cuisines: Salad, Gluten-Free
Average price: $11-30
Area: Back Bay
Address: 659 Boylston St
Boston, MA 02116
Phone: (617) 936-3464

#273
Puritan & Company
Cuisines: American, Cocktail Bar
Average price: $31-60
Area: Inman Square
Address: 1166 Cambridge St
Cambridge, MA 02139
Phone: (617) 615-6195

#274
Clio Restaurant
Cuisines: American, Seafood
Average price: Above $61
Area: Back Bay
Address: 370 Commonwealth Ave
Boston, MA 02215
Phone: (617) 536-7200

#275
New Saigon Sandwich
Cuisines: Deli, Vietnamese
Average price: Under $10
Area: Chinatown
Address: 696 Washington St
Boston, MA 02111
Phone: (617) 542-6296

#276
J J Foley's Cafe
Cuisines: Pub, American
Average price: $11-30
Area: South End
Address: 117 E Berkeley St
Boston, MA 02118
Phone: (617) 728-9101

#277
The Squealing Pig
Cuisines: Pub, Breakfast & Brunch
Average price: $11-30
Area: Mission Hill
Address: 134 Smith St
Roxbury Crossing, MA 02120
Phone: (617) 566-6651

#278
Cafe Kiraz
Cuisines: Sandwiches, Deli
Average price: Under $10
Area: Inman Square
Address: 119 Hampshire St
Cambridge, MA 02139
Phone: (617) 868-2233

#279
Scullers Jazz Club
Cuisines: Jazz & Blues, American
Average price: $11-30
Area: Allston/Brighton
Address: 400 Soldiers Rd
Boston, MA 02134
Phone: (617) 562-4111

#280
75 Chestnut
Cuisines: American, Diner
Average price: $11-30
Area: Beacon Hill
Address: 75 Chestnut St
Boston, MA 02108
Phone: (617) 227-2175

#281
The Blue Room
Cuisines: Mediterranean
Average price: $31-60
Area: Kendall Square/MIT
Address: 1 Kendall Sq, Ste 200
Cambridge, MA 02139
Phone: (617) 494-9034

#282
Brookline Lunch
Cuisines: Diner, Middle Eastern
Average price: Under $10
Area: Central Square
Address: 9 Brookline St
Cambridge, MA 02138
Phone: (617) 354-2983

#283
City Bar
Cuisines: Lounge, American
Average price: $31-60
Area: Back Bay
Address: 61 Exeter St
Boston, MA 02199
Phone: (617) 536-5300

#284
La Famiglia Giorgio's
Cuisines: Italian, Gluten-Free
Average price: $11-30
Area: North End
Address: 112 Salem St
Boston, MA 02113
Phone: (617) 367-6711

#285
Fiore's Bakery
Cuisines: Bakery, Vegan
Average price: Under $10
Area: Jamaica Plain
Address: 55 South St
Jamaica Plain, MA 02130
Phone: (617) 524-9200

#286
Thai Moon
Cuisines: Thai
Average price: $11-30
Area: Arlington Center
Address: 663 Massachusetts Ave
Arlington, MA 02476
Phone: (781) 646-3334

#287
Soul Fire BBQ
Cuisines: Barbeque
Average price: $11-30
Area: Allston/Brighton
Address: 182 Harvard Ave
Allston, MA 02134
Phone: (617) 787-3003

#288
L'Impasto
Cuisines: Italian
Average price: $11-30
Area: North Cambridge
Address: 2263 Massachusetts Ave
Cambridge, MA 02140
Phone: (617) 491-1901

#289
Village Sushi & Grill
Cuisines: Sushi Bar, Japanese
Average price: $11-30
Area: Roslindale Village, Roslindale
Address: 14 Corinth St
Roslindale, MA 02131
Phone: (617) 363-7874

#290
McKenna's Cafe
Cuisines: Breakfast & Brunch
Average price: Under $10
Area: Dorchester
Address: 109 Savin Hill Ave
Dorchester, MA 02125
Phone: (617) 825-8218

#291
Scollay Square
Cuisines: Seafood, American
Average price: $11-30
Area: Downtown, Beacon Hill
Address: 21 Beacon St
Boston, MA 02108
Phone: (617) 742-4900

#292
Paris Crêperie
Cuisines: Crêperie, Caterer
Average price: Under $10
Area: Coolidge Corner
Address: 278 Harvard St
Brookline, MA 02446
Phone: (617) 232-1770

#293
Bon Chon
Cuisines: Korean, Japanese
Average price: $11-30
Area: Allston/Brighton
Address: 123 Brighton Ave
Allston, MA 02134
Phone: (617) 254-8888

#294
The Banshee
Cuisines: Pub, Irish
Average price: $11-30
Area: Dorchester
Address: 934 Dorchester Ave
Dorchester, MA 02125
Phone: (617) 436-9747

#295
Cafe Barada
Cuisines: Caterer, Middle Eastern
Average price: $11-30
Area: North Cambridge
Address: 2269 Massachusetts Ave
Cambridge, MA 02140
Phone: (617) 354-4446

#296
Rod Dee Thai Cuisine
Cuisines: Thai
Average price: Under $10
Area: Porter Square
Address: 1906 Massachusetts Ave
Cambridge, MA 02140
Phone: (617) 374-9252

#297
The Regal Beagle
Cuisines: Bar, American
Average price: $11-30
Area: Coolidge Corner
Address: 308 Harvard St
Brookline, MA 02446
Phone: (617) 739-5151

#298
MJ Ready International Bistro
Cuisines: Thai, Italian
Average price: Under $10
Area: Coolidge Corner
Address: 318 Harvard St
Brookline, MA 02446
Phone: (857) 576-4225

#299
Azama Grill
Cuisines: Middle Eastern, Halal
Average price: Under $10
Area: Allston/Brighton
Address: 54 Harvard Ave
Allston, MA 02134
Phone: (617) 779-0003

#300
Boloco
Cuisines: American
Average price: Under $10
Area: Financial District
Address: 133 Federal St
Boston, MA 02110
Phone: (617) 357-9727

#301
Cafe Sushi
Cuisines: Sushi Bar, Japanese
Average price: $11-30
Area: Harvard Square
Address: 1105 Massachusetts Ave
Cambridge, MA 02138
Phone: (617) 492-0434

#302
Wai Wai Restaurant
Cuisines: Chinese
Average price: Under $10
Area: Chinatown
Address: 26 Oxford St
Boston, MA 02111
Phone: (617) 338-9833

#303
Newtowne Variety
Cuisines: Sandwiches, Salad
Average price: Under $10
Area: Kendall Square/MIT
Address: 93 Windsor St
Cambridge, MA 02139
Phone: (617) 868-5112

#304
Izzy's Restaurant & Sub Shop
Cuisines: American, Sandwiches
Average price: Under $10
Area: Kendall Square/MIT
Address: 169 Harvard St
Cambridge, MA 02139
Phone: (617) 661-3910

#305
Paraiso Restaurant
Cuisines: Spanish
Average price: $11-30
Area: Dorchester, Uphams Corner
Address: 750 Dudley St
Boston, MA 02125
Phone: (617) 265-7067

#306
Tenoch Mexican
Cuisines: Mexican
Average price: Under $10
Area: North End
Address: 3 Lewis St
Boston, MA 02110
Phone: (617) 248-9537

#307
Jac's Cafe
Cuisines: Coffee & Tea,
Breakfast & Brunch
Average price: Under $10
Area: Winthrop
Address: 29 Crest Ave
Winthrop, MA 02152
Phone: (617) 846-7496

#308
Figs
Cuisines: Pizza, Italian
Average price: $11-30
Area: Charlestown
Address: 67 Main St
Charlestown, MA 02129
Phone: (617) 242-2229

#309
Cambridge, 1.
Cuisines: Pizza
Average price: $11-30
Area: Harvard Square
Address: 27 Church St
Cambridge, MA 02138
Phone: (617) 576-1111

#310
Mirisola's
Cuisines: Italian, Pizza
Average price: Under $10
Area: South Boston
Address: 200 L St
Boston, MA 02127
Phone: (617) 269-9701

#311
Tasty Burger
Cuisines: Burgers, Hot Dogs
Average price: Under $10
Area: Fenway
Address: 1301-05 Boylston St
Boston, MA 02215
Phone: (617) 425-4444

#312
Saigon Hut
Cuisines: Vietnamese
Average price: Under $10
Area: East Boston
Address: 305 Meridian St East
Boston, MA 02128
Phone: (617) 567-1944

#313
Mela
Cuisines: Indian
Average price: $11-30
Area: South End
Address: 578 Tremont St
Boston, MA 02118
Phone: (617) 859-4805

#314
Cambridge Common
Cuisines: American, Bar
Average price: $11-30
Area: Porter Square
Address: 1667 Massachusetts Ave
Cambridge, MA 02138
Phone: (617) 547-1228

#315
Citizen Public House & Oyster Bar
Cuisines: Gastropub
Average price: $31-60
Area: Fenway
Address: 1310 Boylston St
Boston, MA 02215
Phone: (617) 450-9000

#316
Sophia's Grotto
Cuisines: Italian, Spanish
Average price: $11-30
Area: Roslindale Village, Roslindale
Address: 22 Birch St
Roslindale, MA 02131
Phone: (617) 323-4595

#317
Anna's Taqueria
Cuisines: Mexican
Average price: Under $10
Area: Davis Square
Address: 236 Elm St
Somerville, MA 02144
Phone: (617) 666-3900

#318
Mehak
Cuisines: Indian, Pakistani
Average price: $11-30
Area: East Boston
Address: 329 Sumner St
Boston, MA 02128
Phone: (617) 567-1900

#319
West Side Lounge
Cuisines: Lounge, American
Average price: $11-30
Area: Porter Square
Address: 1680 Massachusetts Ave
Cambridge, MA 02138
Phone: (617) 441-5566

#320
Lucky's Lounge
Cuisines: Lounge, American
Average price: $11-30
Area: Waterfront, South Boston
Address: 355 Congress St
Boston, MA 02210
Phone: (617) 357-5825

#321
Centre Street Café
Cuisines: Breakfast & Brunch
Average price: $11-30
Area: Jamaica Plain
Address: 669A Centre St
Boston, MA 02130
Phone: (617) 524-9217

#322
Angelo's Pizza
Cuisines: Pizza
Average price: Under $10
Area: Harvard Square
Address: 444 Broadway
Cambridge, MA 02138
Phone: (617) 661-8049

#323
Matt Murphy's Pub
Cuisines: Pub, Irish
Average price: $11-30
Area: Brookline Village
Address: 14 Harvard St
Brookline, MA 02445
Phone: (617) 232-0188

#324
Baraka Café
Cuisines: African, Mediterranean
Average price: $11-30
Area: Central Square
Address: 80 Pearl St
Cambridge, MA 02139
Phone: (617) 868-3951

#325
Sakanaya
Cuisines: Seafood, Japanese
Average price: $11-30
Area: Allston/Brighton
Address: 75 Linden St
Boston, MA 02134
Phone: (617) 254-0009

#326
Los Amigos
Cuisines: Tex-Mex, Mexican
Average price: Under $10
Area: West Roxbury Center
Address: 1743 Centre St
West Roxbury, MA 02132
Phone: (617) 477-4472

#327
Temple Bar
Cuisines: American, Bar
Average price: $11-30
Area: Porter Square
Address: 1688 Massachusetts Ave
Cambridge, MA 02138
Phone: (617) 547-5055

#328
Davio's
Cuisines: Italian, Steakhouse
Average price: $31-60
Area: Back Bay
Address: 75 Arlington St
Boston, MA 02116
Phone: (617) 357-4810

#329
DBar
Cuisines: Dance Club, American
Average price: $11-30
Area: Dorchester
Address: 1236 Dorchester Ave
Dorchester, MA 02125
Phone: (617) 265-4490

#330
May's Fusion and Cuisine
Cuisines: Taiwanese
Average price: $11-30
Area: Allston/Brighton
Address: 95 Glenville Ave
Allston, MA 02134
Phone: (617) 782-1688

#331
Q Restaurant
Cuisines: Chinese, Sushi Bar
Average price: $11-30
Area: Chinatown
Address: 660 Washington St
Boston, MA 02111
Phone: (857) 350-3968

#332
Olga's Kafe
Cuisines: Coffee & Tea
Average price: Under $10
Area: Financial District
Address: 99 Summer St
Boston, MA 02110
Phone: (617) 204-9808

#333
Gourmet Dumpling House
Cuisines: Chinese, Taiwanese
Average price: $11-30
Area: Chinatown
Address: 52 Beach St
Boston, MA 02111
Phone: (617) 338-6223

#334
Trident Booksellers & Café
Cuisines: Bookstore,
Breakfast & Brunch
Average price: $11-30
Area: Back Bay
Address: 338 Newbury St
Boston, MA 02115
Phone: (617) 267-8688

#335
OggiGourmet
Cuisines: Pizza, Sandwiches
Average price: Under $10
Area: Harvard Square
Address: 1350 Massachusetts Ave
Cambridge, MA 02138
Phone: (617) 830-6657

#336
Olé Mexican Grill
Cuisines: Mexican
Average price: $31-60
Area: Inman Square
Address: 11 Springfield St
Cambridge, MA 02139
Phone: (617) 492-4495

#337
Central Kitchen
Cuisines: American
Average price: $31-60
Area: Central Square
Address: 567 Massachusetts Ave
Cambridge, MA 02139
Phone: (617) 491-5599

#338
Sushi Station
Cuisines: Japanese, Sushi Bar
Average price: $11-30
Area: Mission Hill
Address: 1562 Tremont St
Boston, MA 02120
Phone: (617) 738-0888

#339
Border Café
Cuisines: Tex-Mex, Cajun/Creole
Average price: $11-30
Area: Harvard Square
Address: 32 Church St
Cambridge, MA 02138
Phone: (617) 864-6100

#340
Kitchen
Cuisines: American
Average price: $31-60
Area: South End
Address: 560 Tremont St
Boston, MA 02118
Phone: (617) 695-1250

#341
The Courtyard Restaurant
Cuisines: American
Average price: $11-30
Area: Back Bay
Address: 230 Darmouth St
Boston, MA 02116
Phone: (617) 859-2282

#342
Pedro's Tacos
Cuisines: Mexican
Average price: Under $10
Area: Downtown
Address: 55 Bromfield St
Boston, MA 02108
Phone: (617) 482-8822

#343
Corner Cafe
Cuisines: Dive Bar, American
Average price: Under $10
Area: North End
Address: 87 Prince St
Boston, MA 02113
Phone: (617) 523-8997

#344
Himalayan Bistro
Cuisines: Himalayan/Nepalese, Indian
Average price: $11-30
Area: West Roxbury Center,
Address: 1735 Center St
West Roxbury, MA 02132
Phone: (617) 325-3500

#345
Henrietta's Table
Cuisines: American, Desserts
Average price: $31-60
Area: Harvard Square
Address: 1 Bennett St
Cambridge, MA 02138
Phone: (617) 661-5005

#346
Evoo Restaurant
Cuisines: American
Average price: $31-60
Area: East Cambridge
Address: 350 3rd St
Cambridge, MA 02142
Phone: (617) 661-3866

#347
Viga Eatery & Catering
Cuisines: Italian, Sandwiches
Average price: Under $10
Area: Financial District
Address: 133 Pearl St
Boston, MA 02110
Phone: (617) 482-1112

#348
Banh Mi Ba Le
Cuisines: Vietnamese, Sandwiches
Average price: Under $10
Area: Dorchester
Address: 1052 Dorchester Ave
Dorchester, MA 02125
Phone: (617) 265-7171

#349
Les Zygomates
Cuisines: French, Jazz & Blues
Average price: $31-60
Area: Waterfront, Leather District
Address: 129 South St
Boston, MA 02111
Phone: (617) 542-5108

#350
My Thai Vegan Cafe
Cuisines: Thai, Vegan
Average price: $11-30
Area: Chinatown
Address: 3 Beach St
Boston, MA 02111
Phone: (617) 451-2395

#351
Teranga
Cuisines: Bar, Senegalese
Average price: $11-30
Area: South End
Address: 1746 Washington St
Boston, MA 02118
Phone: (617) 266-0003

#352
Legal Harborside
Cuisines: Seafood, American
Average price: $31-60
Area: Waterfront, South Boston
Address: 270 Northern Ave
Boston, MA 02210
Phone: (617) 477-2900

#353
Johnny D's
Cuisines: Bar, Breakfast & Brunch
Average price: $11-30
Area: Davis Square
Address: 17 Holland St
Somerville, MA 02144
Phone: (617) 776-2004

#354
Hong Kong Eatery
Cuisines: Cantonese
Average price: Under $10
Area: Chinatown
Address: 79 Harrison Ave
Boston, MA 02111
Phone: (617) 423-0838

#355
Redbones
Cuisines: Barbeque, Bar
Average price: $11-30
Area: Davis Square
Address: 55 Chester St
Somerville, MA 02144
Phone: (617) 628-2200

#356
Tango Restaurant
Cuisines: Latin American, Steakhouse
Average price: $31-60
Area: Arlington Center
Address: 464 Massachusetts Ave
Arlington, MA 02474
Phone: (781) 443-9000

#357
Grasshopper Restaurant
Cuisines: Chinese, Vietnamese
Average price: $11-30
Area: Allston/Brighton
Address: 1 N Beacon St
Allston, MA 02134
Phone: (617) 254-8883

#358
Cafe Fleuri
Cuisines: French, Café
Average price: $31-60
Area: Financial District
Address: 250 Franklin St
Boston, MA 02110
Phone: (617) 451-1900

#359
JP Seafood Cafe
Cuisines: Japanese, Korean
Average price: $11-30
Area: Jamaica Plain
Address: 730 Ctr St
Jamaica Plain, MA 02130
Phone: (617) 983-5177

#360
Tremont 647
Cuisines: Bar, American
Average price: $11-30
Area: South End
Address: 647 Tremont St
Boston, MA 02118
Phone: (617) 266-4600

#361
Legal Sea Foods
Cuisines: Seafood
Average price: $11-30
Area: East Boston
Address: 1 Harborside Dr
Boston, MA 02128
Phone: (617) 568-2811

#362
Shabu-Zen
Cuisines: Japanese
Average price: $11-30
Area: Allston/Brighton
Address: 80 Brighton Ave
Allston, MA 02134
Phone: (617) 782-8888

#363
Mooo....
Cuisines: Steakhouse
Average price: Above $61
Area: Downtown
Address: 15 Beacon St
Boston, MA 02108
Phone: (617) 670-2515

#364
Jo Jo TaiPei
Cuisines: Taiwanese, Chinese
Average price: $11-30
Area: Allston/Brighton
Address: 103 Brighton Ave
Allston, MA 02134
Phone: (617) 254-8889

#365
My Cousin's Place
Cuisines: Café, Coffee & Tea
Average price: Under $10
Area: North End
Address: 396 Hanover St
Boston, MA 02113
Phone: (857) 350-3029

#366
Vee Vee
Cuisines: American
Average price: $11-30
Area: Jamaica Plain
Address: 763 Centre St
Jamaica Plain, MA 02130
Phone: (617) 522-0145

#367
Liberty Bell Roast Beef
Cuisines: Sandwiches, Pizza
Average price: Under $10
Area: South Boston
Address: 170 W Broadway
Boston, MA 02127
Phone: (617) 269-3909

#368
Little Q Hot Pot
Cuisines: Chinese
Average price: $11-30
Area: East Arlington
Address: 196 Massachusetts Ave
Arlington, MA 02474
Phone: (781) 488-3755

#369
Terramia Ristorante
Cuisines: Italian
Average price: $31-60
Area: North End
Address: 98 Salem St
Boston, MA 02113
Phone: (617) 523-3112

#370
Shanghai Gate
Cuisines: Chinese
Average price: $11-30
Area: Allston/Brighton
Address: 204 Harvard Ave
Allston, MA 02134
Phone: (617) 566-7344

#371
Masa
Cuisines: American, Mexican
Average price: $11-30
Area: South End
Address: 439 Tremont St
Boston, MA 02116
Phone: (617) 338-8884

#372
Felipe's Taqueria
Cuisines: Mexican
Average price: Under $10
Area: Harvard Square
Address: 83 Mt Auburn St
Cambridge, MA 02138
Phone: (617) 354-9944

#373
Lolita Cocina & Tequila Bar
Cuisines: Mexican, Lounge
Average price: $31-60
Area: Back Bay
Address: 271 Dartmouth St
Boston, MA 02116
Phone: (617) 369-5609

#374
Carmelina's
Cuisines: Italian
Average price: $31-60
Area: North End
Address: 307 Hanover St
Boston, MA 02113
Phone: (617) 742-0020

#375
Antico Forno
Cuisines: Italian
Average price: $11-30
Area: North End
Address: 93 Salem St
Boston, MA 02113
Phone: (617) 723-6733

#376
**Alfredo's Italian Kitchen
South Boston**
Cuisines: Italian, Pizza
Average price: Under $10
Area: South Boston
Address: 243 Dorchester St South
Boston, MA 02127
Phone: (617) 268-8939

#377
Pikaichi
Cuisines: Japanese
Average price: Under $10
Area: Allston/Brighton
Address: 1 Brighton Ave
Boston, MA 02134
Phone: (617) 789-4818

#378
Toscano
Cuisines: Italian
Average price: $11-30
Area: Harvard Square
Address: 52 Brattle St
Cambridge, MA 02138
Phone: (617) 354-5250

#379
Local 149
Cuisines: Pub, American
Average price: $11-30
Area: South Boston
Address: 149 P St
Boston, MA 02127
Phone: (617) 269-0900

#380
The Field
Cuisines: Pub, Burgers
Average price: Under $10
Area: Central Square
Address: 20 Prospect St
Cambridge, MA 02139
Phone: (617) 354-7345

#381
Baltic Deli & Cafe
Cuisines: Deli, Ethnic Food
Average price: Under $10
Area: South Boston
Address: 632 Dorchester Ave
Boston, MA 02127
Phone: (617) 268-2435

#382
Sabur
Cuisines: Mediterranean
Average price: $31-60
Area: Teele Square
Address: 212 Holland St
Somerville, MA 02144
Phone: (617) 776-7890

#383
Fill-A-Buster
Cuisines: Deli, Salad
Average price: Under $10
Area: Downtown, Beacon Hill
Address: 142 Bowdoin St
Boston, MA 02108
Phone: (617) 523-8164

#384
Alex's Chimis
Cuisines: Caribbean
Average price: Under $10
Area: Jamaica Plain
Address: 358 Centre St
Jamaica Plain, MA 02130
Phone: (617) 522-5201

#385
Sweet Touch Cafe
Cuisines: Coffee & Tea, Sandwiches
Average price: Under $10
Area: East Cambridge
Address: 241 Cambridge St
Cambridge, MA 02141
Phone: (617) 491-4119

#386
Harry's Bar & Grill
Cuisines: Bar, American
Average price: $11-30
Area: Allston/Brighton
Address: 1430 Commonwealth Ave
Brighton, MA 02135
Phone: (617) 738-9990

#387
Spike's Junkyard Dogs
Cuisines: Hot Dogs
Average price: Under $10
Area: Allston/Brighton
Address: 108 Brighton Ave
Allston, MA 02134
Phone: (617) 254-7700

#388
Back Bay Sandwich
Cuisines: Sandwiches
Average price: Under $10
Area: Back Bay
Address: 31 St James Ave
Boston, MA 02116
Phone: (617) 451-1561

#389
Tangierino
Cuisines: Moroccan, African
Average price: $31-60
Area: Charlestown
Address: 83 Main St
Charlestown, MA 02129
Phone: (617) 242-6009

#390
Carmen Trattoria
Cuisines: Italian
Average price: $31-60
Area: North End
Address: 33 North Sq
Boston, MA 02113
Phone: (617) 742-6421

#391
Addis Red Sea
Cuisines: Ethiopian
Average price: $11-30
Area: South End
Address: 544 Tremont St
Boston, MA 02116
Phone: (617) 426-8727

#392
La Summa
Cuisines: Italian
Average price: $11-30
Area: North End
Address: 30 Fleet St
Boston, MA 02113
Phone: (617) 523-9503

#393
Neighborhoods Coffee & Crepes
Cuisines: Coffee & Tea, Café
Average price: Under $10
Area: Fenway
Address: 96 Peterborough St
Boston, MA 02215
Phone: (617) 262-7700

#394
Dough East Boston
Cuisines: Pizza, Sandwiches
Average price: Under $10
Area: East Boston
Address: 20 Maverick St East
Boston, MA 02128
Phone: (617) 567-8787

#395
Viga Italian Eatery & Caterer
Cuisines: Italian
Average price: Under $10
Area: Downtown
Address: 291 Devonshire St
Boston, MA 02110
Phone: (617) 482-1113

#396
Qing Dao Garden
Cuisines: Chinese, Seafood
Average price: $11-30
Area: North Cambridge
Address: 2382 Massachusetts Ave
Cambridge, MA 02138
Phone: (617) 492-7540

#397
Berkeley Perk Cafe
Cuisines: Sandwiches, Coffee & Tea
Average price: Under $10
Area: South End
Address: 69 Berkeley St
Boston, MA 02116
Phone: (617) 426-7375

#398
Harvest of India
Cuisines: Indian, Pakistani
Average price: $11-30
Area: Central Square
Address: 1001 Massachusetts Ave
Cambridge, MA 02138
Phone: (617) 441-4034

#399
Myung Dong 1st Ave
Cuisines: Korean, Bar
Average price: $11-30
Area: Allston/Brighton
Address: 90-92 Harvard Ave
Allston, MA 02134
Phone: (617) 206-3229

#400
Dado Tea
Cuisines: Coffee & Tea, Sandwiches
Average price: Under $10
Area: Central Square
Address: 955 Massachusetts Ave
Cambridge, MA 02139
Phone: (617) 497-9061

#401
Cactus Mexican Grill
Cuisines: Mexican
Average price: Under $10
Area: East Boston
Address: 44 Maverick Sq
Boston, MA 02128
Phone: (617) 561-2800

#402
Stoddard's Fine Food & Ale
Cuisines: Bar, American
Average price: $11-30
Area: Downtown
Address: 48 Temple Pl
Boston, MA 02111
Phone: (617) 426-0048

#403
The Pour House
Cuisines: Bar, American
Average price: Under $10
Area: Back Bay
Address: 907 Boylston St
Boston, MA 02115
Phone: (617) 236-1767

#404
Grass Roots Cafe
Cuisines: Sandwiches, Korean
Average price: Under $10
Area: Downtown
Address: 101 Arch St
Boston, MA 02110
Phone: (617) 951-2124

#405
The Goods JP
Cuisines: American
Average price: Under $10
Area: Jamaica Plain
Address: 378 Centre St
Boston, MA 02130
Phone: (617) 522-1210

#406
Estragon
Cuisines: Tapas Bar, Spanish
Average price: $11-30
Area: South End
Address: 700 Harrison Ave
Boston, MA 02118
Phone: (617) 266-0443

#407
Five Horses Tavern
Cuisines: American, Pub
Average price: $11-30
Area: Davis Square
Address: 400 Highland Ave
Somerville, MA 02144
Phone: (617) 764-1655

#408
Knight Moves
Cuisines: Café
Average price: Under $10
Area: Coolidge Corner
Address: 1402 Beacon St
Brookline, MA 02446
Phone: (617) 487-5259

#409
ZuZu
Cuisines: Mediterranean, Italian
Average price: $11-30
Area: Central Square
Address: 474 Massachusetts Ave
Cambridge, MA 02139
Phone: (617) 864-3278

#410
Regina Pizzeria
Cuisines: Pizza, Italian
Average price: $11-30
Area: Allston/Brighton
Address: 353 Cambridge Street
Allston, MA 02134
Phone: (617) 783-2300

#411
Ostra
Cuisines: Seafood, Mediterranean
Average price: Above $61
Area: Back Bay
Address: 1 Charles St S
Boston, MA 02116
Phone: (617) 421-1200

#412
Cambridge Deli & Grill
Cuisines: Deli, American
Average price: Under $10
Area: Central Square
Address: 90 River St
Cambridge, MA 02139
Phone: (617) 868-6740

#413
The Goods JP
Cuisines: American
Average price: Under $10
Area: Jamaica Plain
Address: 378 Centre St
Boston, MA 02130
Phone: (617) 522-1210

#414
163 Vietnamese
Sandwiches & Bubble Tea
Cuisines: Vietnamese, Coffee & Tea
Average price: Under $10
Area: Chinatown
Address: 66 Harrison Ave
Boston, MA 02111
Phone: (617) 542-7903

#415
Nico Ristorante
Cuisines: Italian
Average price: $31-60
Area: North End
Address: 417 Hanover St
Boston, MA 02113
Phone: (617) 742-0404

#416
Rialto
Cuisines: Italian
Average price: $31-60
Area: Harvard Square
Address: 1 Bennett St
Cambridge, MA 02138
Phone: (617) 661-5050

#417
Cafe Mamtaz
Cuisines: Indian
Average price: $11-30
Area: South Boston
Address: 87 L St
Boston, MA 02127
Phone: (617) 464-4800

#418
Tip Tap Room
Cuisines: American, Bar
Average price: $11-30
Area: Beacon Hill
Address: 138 Cambridge St
Boston, MA 02114
Phone: (857) 350-3344

#419
Lucca
Cuisines: Italian
Average price: $31-60
Area: North End
Address: 226 Hanover St
Boston, MA 02113
Phone: (617) 742-9200

#420
Christopher's
Cuisines: Bar, American
Average price: $11-30
Area: Porter Square
Address: 1920 Massachusetts Ave
Cambridge, MA 02140
Phone: (617) 876-9180

#421
Hidyan Café
Cuisines: Ice Cream
Average price: Under $10
Area: Fenway
Address: 80 Kilmarnock St
Boston, MA 02215
Phone: (617) 437-0966

#422
Aceituna Cafe
Cuisines: Middle Eastern
Average price: Under $10
Area: East Cambridge
Address: 605 W Kendall St
Cambridge, MA 02142
Phone: (617) 252-0707

#423
Peach Farm
Cuisines: Chinese
Average price: $11-30
Area: Chinatown
Address: 4 Tyler St
Boston, MA 02111
Phone: (617) 482-1116

#424
Sabatino's Italian Kitchen
Cuisines: Italian, Pizza
Average price: Under $10
Area: East Arlington
Address: 242 Massachusetts Ave
Arlington, MA 02476
Phone: (781) 646-4126

#425
Strega Waterfront
Cuisines: Italian
Average price: $31-60
Area: Waterfront, South Boston
Address: One Marina Park Dr
Boston, MA 02210
Phone: (617) 345-3992

#426
Viga
Cuisines: Italian
Average price: Under $10
Area: Back Bay
Address: 304 Stuart St
Boston, MA 02116
Phone: (617) 542-7200

#427
City Landing
Cuisines: American
Average price: $31-60
Area: Waterfront
Address: 255 State St
Boston, MA 02109
Phone: (617) 725-0305

#428
Frio Rico
Cuisines: Latin American, Grocery
Average price: Under $10
Area: East Boston
Address: 360 R Bennington St East
Boston, MA 02128
Phone: (617) 569-1505

#429
Mare
Cuisines: Italian, Seafood
Average price: $31-60
Area: North End
Address: 135 Richmond St
Boston, MA 02109
Phone: (617) 723-6273

#430
Boston Kabob Company
Cuisines: Middle Eastern, Halal
Average price: Under $10
Area: Allston/Brighton
Address: 164 Brighton Ave
Allston, MA 02134
Phone: (617) 254-2333

#431
Tavern at the End of the World
Cuisines: Pub, American
Average price: $11-30
Area: Charlestown
Address: 108 Cambridge St
Charlestown, MA 02129
Phone: (617) 241-4999

#432
Stephi's on Tremont
Cuisines: American
Average price: $11-30
Area: South End
Address: 571 Tremont St
Boston, MA 02118
Phone: (617) 236-2063

#433
James Gate
Cuisines: Pub, American
Average price: $11-30
Area: Jamaica Plain
Address: 5 McBride St
Jamaica Plain, MA 02130
Phone: (617) 983-2000

#434
Casa Romero
Cuisines: Mexican
Average price: $11-30
Area: Back Bay
Address: 30 Gloucester St
Boston, MA 02115
Phone: (617) 536-4341

#435
Thelonious Monkfish
Cuisines: Sushi Bar, Japanese
Average price: $11-30
Area: Central Square
Address: 524 Massachusetts Ave
Cambridge, MA 02139
Phone: (617) 441-2116

#436
Saraceno
Cuisines: Italian
Average price: $11-30
Area: North End
Address: 286 Hanover St
Boston, MA 02113
Phone: (617) 227-5353

#437
Maurizios
Cuisines: Italian
Average price: $11-30
Area: North End
Address: 364 Hanover St
Boston, MA 02113
Phone: (617) 367-1123

#438
New Jumbo Seafood Restaurant
Cuisines: Seafood, Chinese
Average price: $11-30
Area: Chinatown
Address: 5-9 Hudson St
Boston, MA 02111
Phone: (617) 542-2823

#439
Battery Park Bar & Lounge
Cuisines: American, Lounge
Average price: $11-30
Area: Financial District
Address: 33 Batterymarch St
Boston, MA 02110
Phone: (617) 350-7275

#440
Cafe Beirut
Cuisines: Lebanese
Average price: Under $10
Area: Jamaica Plain
Address: 654 Centre St
Jamaica Plain, MA 02130
Phone: (617) 522-7264

#441
Legal Sea Foods
Cuisines: Seafood
Average price: $31-60
Area: Waterfront
Address: 255 State St
Boston, MA 02109
Phone: (617) 742-5300

#442
Pat's Pizza
Cuisines: Pizza
Average price: Under $10
Area: Dorchester
Address: 2254 Dorchester Ave
Dorchester Center, MA 02124
Phone: (617) 298-9625

#443
Buccieri's Cafe
Cuisines: Italian, Deli
Average price: Under $10
Area: Financial District
Address: 260 Franklin St
Boston, MA 02110
Phone: (617) 330-5355

#444
MuLan
Cuisines: Taiwanese
Average price: $11-30
Area: Kendall Square/MIT
Address: 228 Broadway
Cambridge, MA 02139
Phone: (617) 441-8812

#445
Violette Gluten Free Bakery
Cuisines: Bakery, Coffee & Tea
Average price: $11-30
Area: Central Square
Address: 1001 Massachusetts Ave
Cambridge, MA 02139
Phone: (617) 945-7660

#446
OTTO
Cuisines: Pizza
Average price: $11-30
Area: Coolidge Corner
Address: 289 Harvard St
Brookline, MA 02446
Phone: (617) 232-0014

#447
**Del Frisco's Double Eagle
Steak House**
Cuisines: Seafood, Steakhouse
Average price: Above $61
Area: Waterfront, South Boston
Address: 250 Northern Ave
Boston, MA 02210
Phone: (617) 951-1368

#448
Singh's Roti Shop
Cuisines: Caribbean
Average price: Under $10
Area: Dorchester
Address: 692 Columbia Rd
Dorchester, MA 02125
Phone: (617) 282-7977

#449
Royal Roast Beef & Seafood
Cuisines: Seafood, American
Average price: Under $10
Area: East Boston
Address: 752 Bennington St
Boston, MA 02128
Phone: (617) 567-7779

#450
Que Padre
Cuisines: Mexican
Average price: Under $10
Area: East Boston
Address: 386 Chelsea St
Boston, MA 02128
Phone: (617) 418-7278

#451
Maggiano's Little Italy
Cuisines: Italian
Average price: $11-30
Area: Back Bay
Address: 4 Columbus Ave
Boston, MA 02116
Phone: (617) 542-3456

#452
Ward 8
Cuisines: Cocktail Bar, American
Average price: $11-30
Area: North End
Address: 90 N Washington St
Boston, MA 02113
Phone: (617) 823-4478

#453
El Paisa Orient Heights
Cuisines: Colombian
Average price: $11-30
Area: East Boston
Address: 1012 Bennington St
Boston, MA 02128
Phone: (617) 569-5267

#454
The Warren Tavern
Cuisines: Bar, American
Average price: $11-30
Area: Charlestown
Address: 2 Pleasant St
Charlestown, MA 02129
Phone: (617) 241-8142

#455
Bon Chon
Cuisines: Korean, Barbeque
Average price: $11-30
Area: Harvard Square
Address: 57 John F Kennedy St
Cambridge, MA 02138
Phone: (617) 868-0981

#456
Phu-ket Thai
Cuisines: Thai
Average price: $11-30
Area: West Roxbury Center
Address: 1856 Centre St
West Roxbury, MA 02132
Phone: (617) 469-5200

#457
Mr. Bartley's Gourmet Burgers
Cuisines: Burgers
Average price: $11-30
Area: Harvard Square
Address: 1246 Massachusetts Ave
Cambridge, MA 02138
Phone: (617) 354-6559

#458
The Maharaja
Cuisines: Indian
Average price: $11-30
Area: Harvard Square
Address: 57 JFK St
Cambridge, MA 02138
Phone: (617) 547-2757

#459
Rendezvous In Central Square
Cuisines: American
Average price: $31-60
Area: Central Square
Address: 502 Massachusetts Ave
Cambridge, MA 02139
Phone: (617) 576-1900

#460
Thaitation
Cuisines: Thai
Average price: $11-30
Area: Fenway
Address: 129 Jersey St
Boston, MA 02215
Phone: (617) 585-9909

#461
Café Jaffa
Cuisines: Middle Eastern
Average price: $11-30
Area: Back Bay
Address: 48 Gloucester St
Boston, MA 02115
Phone: (617) 536-0230

#462
Bravo Pizza
Cuisines: Pizza, Ice Cream
& Frozen Yogurt
Average price: Under $10
Area: Allston/Brighton
Address: 160 Brighton Ave
Allston, MA 02134
Phone: (617) 782-0882

#463
Yokohama
Cuisines: Sushi Bar, Japanese
Average price: $11-30
Area: Brookline Village
Address: 238 Washington St
Brookline, MA 02445
Phone: (617) 734-6465

#464
UBurger
Cuisines: Burgers
Average price: Under $10
Area: Allston/Brighton
Address: 1022 Commonwealth Ave
Boston, MA 02215
Phone: (617) 487-4855

#465
Omni Parker House
Cuisines: Hotel, Breakfast & Brunch
Average price: $31-60
Area: Downtown
Address: 60 School St
Boston, MA 02108
Phone: (617) 227-8600

#466
Hot Pot Buffet
Cuisines: Chinese, Buffet
Average price: $11-30
Area: Chinatown
Address: 70 Beach St
Boston, MA 02111
Phone: (617) 338-0808

#467
Sister Sorel
Cuisines: Bar, American
Average price: $11-30
Area: South End
Address: 645 Tremont St
Boston, MA 02116
Phone: (617) 266-4600

#468
Smith & Wollensky
Cuisines: Steakhouse
Average price: Above $61
Area: Waterfront, South Boston
Address: 294 Congress St
Boston, MA 02210
Phone: (617) 778-2200

#469
Tampopo
Cuisines: Japanese
Average price: Under $10
Area: Porter Square
Address: 1815 Massachusetts Ave
Cambridge, MA 02140
Phone: (617) 868-5457

#470
T Anthony's Pizzeria & Restaurant
Cuisines: Pizza, Italian
Average price: Under $10
Area: Allston/Brighton
Address: 1016 Commonwealth Ave
Boston, MA 02215
Phone: (617) 734-7708

#471
Bon Me
Cuisines: Food Stand, Vietnamese
Average price: Under $10
Area: Downtown
Address: 602 Commonwealth Ave
Boston, MA 02215
Phone: (617) 945-2615

#472
Oliveiras Restaurant East Boston
Cuisines: Brazilian, Barbeque
Average price: $11-30
Area: East Boston
Address: 297 Chelsea St
Boston, MA 02128
Phone: (617) 561-7277

#473
Stoli Bar & Restaurant
Cuisines: Russian, Lounge
Average price: $31-60
Area: Brookline Village
Address: 213 Washington St
Brookline, MA 02445
Phone: (617) 731-5070

#474
Same Old Place
Cuisines: Pizza
Average price: Under $10
Area: Jamaica Plain
Address: 662 Ctr St
Jamaica Plain, MA 02130
Phone: (617) 524-9461

#475
The Friendly Toast
Cuisines: Breakfast & Brunch
Average price: $11-30
Area: Kendall Square/MIT
Address: 1 Kendall Sq
Cambridge, MA 02139
Phone: (617) 621-1200

#476
Café de Lulu
Cuisines: Chinese
Average price: Under $10
Area: Chinatown
Address: 42 Beach St
Boston, MA 02111
Phone: (617) 391-0888

#477
Habanero Mexican Grill
Cuisines: Mexican
Average price: Under $10
Area: Allston/Brighton
Address: 166 Brighton Ave
Boston, MA 02134
Phone: (617) 254-0299

#478
Beauty's
Cuisines: Pizza
Average price: Under $10
Area: Kendall Square/MIT
Address: 228 Broadway
Cambridge, MA 02139
Phone: (617) 876-6969

#479
Beauty's
Cuisines: Pizza
Average price: Under $10
Area: Kendall Square/MIT
Address: 228 Broadway
Cambridge, MA 02139
Phone: (617) 876-6969

#480
Pit Stop Barbeque
Cuisines: Barbeque
Average price: $11-30
Area: Mattapan
Address: 888A Morton St
Dorchester, MA 02124
Phone: (617) 436-0485

#481
Grasshopper Cafe
Cuisines: Sandwiches,
Breakfast & Brunch
Average price: $11-30
Area: Charlestown
Address: 229-231 Bunker Hill St
Boston, MA 02129
Phone: (617) 242-0000

#482
Papagayo
Cuisines: Mexican
Average price: $11-30
Area: Waterfront, South Boston
Address: 283 Summer St
Boston, MA 02210
Phone: (617) 423-1000

#483
Sweet Cheeks
Cuisines: Southern, Bar
Average price: $11-30
Area: Fenway
Address: 1381 Boylston St
Boston, MA 02215
Phone: (617) 266-1300

#484
Moody's Falafel Palace
Cuisines: Falafel
Average price: Under $10
Area: Central Square
Address: 25 Central Sq
Cambridge, MA 02139
Phone: (617) 864-0827

#485
Boston Chops
Cuisines: Bar, Steakhouse
Average price: $31-60
Area: South End
Address: 1375 Washington St
Boston, MA 02118
Phone: (617) 227-5011

#486
Algiers Coffee House
Cuisines: Coffee & Tea, Middle Eastern
Average price: $11-30
Area: Harvard Square
Address: 40 Brattle St
Cambridge, MA 02138
Phone: (617) 492-1557

#487
Ghazal Fine Indian Cuisine
Cuisines: Indian
Average price: $11-30
Area: Jamaica Plain
Address: 711 Centre St
Boston, MA 02130
Phone: (617) 522-9500

#488
Uptown Cafe
Cuisines: Italian, Sandwiches
Average price: Under $10
Area: Downtown, Beacon Hill
Address: 120 Cambridge St
Boston, MA 02114
Phone: (617) 227-1181

#489
**The Middle East
Restaurant & Nightclub**
Cuisines: Middle Eastern, Music Venues
Average price: $11-30
Area: Central Square
Address: 472 Massachusetts Ave
Cambridge, MA 02139
Phone: (617) 864-3278

#490
OTTO
Cuisines: Pizza, Bar
Average price: $11-30
Area: Allston/Brighton
Address: 888 Commonwealth Ave
Boston, MA 02215
Phone: (617) 232-0447

#491
Boloco Copley Square
Cuisines: American, Mexican
Average price: Under $10
Area: Back Bay
Address: 569 Boylston St
Boston, MA 02116
Phone: (617) 259-1619

#492
Sonsie
Cuisines: American, Wine Bar
Average price: $31-60
Area: Back Bay
Address: 327 Newbury St
Boston, MA 02115
Phone: (617) 351-2500

#493
Jimmy's Steer House
Cuisines: Steakhouse
Average price: $11-30
Area: Arlington Heights
Address: 1111 Massachusetts Ave
Arlington, MA 02476
Phone: (781) 646-4450

#494
Saloon
Cuisines: American, Pub
Average price: $11-30
Area: Davis Square
Address: 255 Elm St
Somerville, MA 02144
Phone: (617) 628-4444

#495
Charlie's Kitchen
Cuisines: American, Dive Bar
Average price: Under $10
Area: Harvard Square
Address: 10 Eliot St
Cambridge, MA 02138
Phone: (617) 492-9646

#496
Dim Sum Chef
Cuisines: Dim Sum
Average price: Under $10
Area: Allston/Brighton
Address: 1095 Commonwealth Ave
Boston, MA 02215
Phone: (617) 254-2073

#497
Sabatino's Italian
Cuisines: Italian, Pizza
Average price: Under $10
Area: Allston/Brighton
Address: 1443 Commonwealth Ave
Brighton, MA 02135
Phone: (617) 787-9393

#498
Yard House
Cuisines: American
Average price: $11-30
Area: Fenway
Address: 126 Brookline Avenue
Boston, MA 02215
Phone: (617) 236-4083

#499
Petit Robert Bistro
Cuisines: French
Average price: $11-30
Area: South End
Address: 480 Columbus Ave
Boston, MA 02118
Phone: (617) 867-0600

#500
Jamaica Plain House of Pizza
Cuisines: Pizza, Italian
Average price: Under $10
Area: Jamaica Plain
Address: 775 Centre St Jamaica Plain, MA
02130
Phone: (617) 522-4154

TOP 100 ATTRACTIONS

Most Recommended by Locals & Trevelers
Ranking (from #1 to #100)

#1
**Freedom Trail
Foundation Tour**
Tour
Area: Chinatown
Address: 99 Chauncy St
Boston, MA 02111
Phone: (617) 357-8300

#2
Old North Church
Landmark/Historical
Area: North End
Address: 193 Salem St
Boston, MA 02113
Phone: (617) 523-6676

#3
Boston Public Library
Libraries, Venues, Event Space,
Landmark/Historical
Area: Back Bay
Address: 700 Boylston St
Boston, MA 02116
Phone: (617) 536-5400

#4
The Christian Science Plaza
Church, Museum,
Landmark/Historical
Area: Fenway
Address: 210 Massachusetts Ave
Boston, MA 02115

#5
**New England
Holocaust Memorial**
Landmark/Historical
Area: Downtown
Address: Congress St
Boston, MA 02109

#6
Skywalk Observatory
Landmark/Historical
Area: Back Bay
Address: 800 Boylston St
Boston, MA 02199
Phone: (617) 859-0648

#7
Faneuil Hall
Landmark/Historical
Area: Downtown
Address: 0 Faneuil Hall Sq
Boston, MA 02109

#8
Old State House
Landmark/Historical, Museum
Area: Downtown
Address: 206 Washington St
Boston, MA 02108
Phone: (617) 720-1713

#9
Massachusetts State House
Landmark/Historical
Area: Beacon Hill
Address: 24 Beacon St
Boston, MA 02133
Phone: (617) 727-7030

#10
**Leonard P. Zakim Bunker Hill
Memorial Bridge**
Landmark/Historical
Area: North End
Address: 100 Beverly St
Boston, MA 02114

#11
Citgo Sign
Landmark/Historical
Area: Allston/Brighton
Address: 666 Beacon St
Boston, MA 02215

#12
Prudential Tower
Landmark/Historical
Area: Back Bay
Address: 800 Boylston St
Boston, MA 02199
Phone: (617) 236-3100

#13
Newbury Street
Landmark/Historical
Area: Back Bay
Address: 10 Newbury St
Boston, MA 02228

#14
John Hancock Tower
Landmark/Historical
Area: Back Bay
Address: 200 Clarendon St
Boston, MA 02228
Phone: (617) 572-6420

#15
Granary Burial Ground
Landmark/Historical,
Funeral Service&Cemetery
Area: Downtown
Address: 101a Tremont St
Boston, MA 02108
Phone: (617) 635-4505

#16
Boston National Historical Park
Local Flavor, Museum, Education,
Landmark/Historical
Address: Charlestown Navy Yard
Boston, MA 02455

#17
Copp's Hill Burying Ground
Landmark/Historical,
Funeral Service&Cemetery
Area: North End
Address: 21 Hull St
Boston, MA 02113

#18
Massachusetts Historical Society
Landmark/Historical
Area: Allston/Brighton
Address: 1154 Boylston St
Boston, MA 02215

#19
Boston Harbor Islands
Park, Beaches,
Landmark/Historical
Area: Waterfront, South Boston
Address: 408 Atlantic Ave, Ste 228
Boston, MA 02110
Phone: (617) 223-8666

#20
King's Chapel
Church, Landmark/Historical
Area: Downtown
Address: 58 Tremont St
Boston, MA 02108
Phone: (617) 523-1749

#21
Longfellow Bridge
Landmark/Historical
Area: Beacon Hill
Address: Longfellow Bridge
Boston, MA 02228
Phone: (617) 973-7000

#22
Ether Dome
Landmark/Historical
Area: North End
Address: Bulfinch Building
Boston, MA 02114

#23
Copley MBTA Station
Landmark/Historical,
Public Transportation
Area: Back Bay
Address: 640 Boylston St at 230
Dartmouth St
Boston, MA 02116
Phone: (617) 222-3200

#24
Long Wharf
Landmark/Historical
Area: Waterfront
Address: Long Wharf
Boston, MA 02110

#25
Bobby Orr Statue
Landmark/Historical
Area: North End
Address: 96 Causeway St
Boston, MA 02114

#26
Boston City Hall
Venues, Event Space,
Landmark/Historical
Area: Downtown
Address: 1 City Hall Plz
Boston, MA 02201
Phone: (617) 635-4000

#27
John Copley Statue
Landmark/Historical
Area: Back Bay
Address: 206 Clarendon St
Boston, MA 02116

#28
Charlestown Navy Yard
Landmark/Historical
Area: Charlestown
Address: Charlestown Navy Yard
Boston, MA 02129

#29
Boston University Bridge
Landmark/Historical
Area: Allston/Brighton
Address: Commonwealth Ave
& Boston Univ Bridge
Boston, MA 02215

#30
The Big Dig
Landmark/Historical, Transportation
Area: Waterfront, South Boston,
Financial District
Address: 500 Atlantic Ave
Boston, MA 02210

#31
Tortoise & The Hare Sculpture
Landmark/Historical
Area: Back Bay
Address: 206 Clarendon St
Boston, MA 02116

#32
Quest Eternal
Landmark/Historical
Area: Back Bay
Address: 800 Boylston St
Boston, MA 02199

#33
Massachusetts State House
Venues, Event Space,
Landmark/Historical
Area: Beacon Hill
Address: State House
Boston, MA 02133
Phone: (617) 727-1100

#34
Arthur Fiedler Footbridge
Landmark/Historical
Area: Beacon Hill
Address: Embankment Rd
& Storrow Dr
Boston, MA 02108

#35
The Tobin Bridge
Landmark/Historical
Area: Back Bay
Address: Tobin Memorial Bridge
Boston, MA 02228

#36
Jamaica Plain
Landmark/Historical
Area: Jamaica Plain
Address: 3712 Washington St
Boston, MA 02130

#37
Bostonian Society Museum Shop
Museum, Landmark/Historical
Area: Downtown
Address: Quincy Market
Boston, MA 02109

#38
Comm Ave - BU Bridge Intersection
Landmark/Historical, Transportation
Area: Allston/Brighton
Address: 791 Commonwealth Ave
Boston, MA 02215

#39
Andrew McArdle Bridge
Landmark/Historical, Local Flavor,
Transportation
Area: East Boston
Address: 41 Andrew McArdle Bridge
Boston, MA 02128

#40
Chelsea Street Bridge
Landmark/Historical
Area: East Boston
Address: 620 Chelsea St
Boston, MA 02128

#41
Bunker Hill Monument
Landmark/Historical
Area: Charlestown
Address: 43 Monument Sq
Charlestown, MA 02129
Phone: (617) 242-5641

#42
Alford Street Bridge
Landmark/Historical
Area: Charlestown
Address: 95-101 Alford St
Boston, MA 02129

#43
Historic New England
Landmark/Historical
Area: North End
Address: 141 Cambridge St
Boston, MA 02114

#44
Historic Bostonian Properties
Landmark/Historical
Area: Beacon Hill
Address: Mount Vernon
Boston, MA 02108
Phone: (617) 720-5077

#45
Emerald Necklace Conservancy
Landmark/Historical
Area: Fenway
Address: 125 Fenway
Boston, MA 02115
Phone: (617) 522-2700

#46
The Bostonian Society
Landmark/Historical
Area: Downtown
Address: 206 Washington St.
Boston, MA 02109
Phone: (617) 720-1713

#47
Old City Hall
Landmark/Historical
Area: Downtown
Address: 45 School St
Boston, MA 02108
Phone: (617) 523-8678

#48
Fenway Studio
Landmark/Historical
Area: Allston/Brighton
Address: 30 Ipswich St Apt 201
Boston, MA 02215

#49
Eastern National
Landmark/Historical
Area: Downtown
Address: 15 State St
Boston, MA 02109

#50
Bay State Road
Landmark/Historical
Area: Allston/Brighton
Address: Bay State Rd
Boston, MA 02215

#51
Lifetips
Landmark/Historical
Area: North End
Address: 240 Commercial St
Boston, MA 02109
Phone: (617) 227-8800

#52
Bostonian Society Museum Shop
Landmark/Historical
Area: Downtown
Address: South Canopy,
Quincy Market Boston, MA 02109

#53
Admiral Farragut
Landmark/Historical
Area: South Boston
Address: E Broadway & William J
Day Blvd Boston, MA 02127

#54
MIT Stata Center
Landmark/Historical
Area: Kendall Square/MIT
Address: 32 Vassar St
Cambridge, MA 02139
Phone: (617) 577-8812

#55
Memorial Hall
Landmark/Historical
Area: Harvard Square
Address: 45 Quincy St
Cambridge, MA 02138
Phone: (617) 496-4595

#56
Harvard Yard
Landmark/Historical
Area: Harvard Square
Address: Harvard University Campus
Cambridge, MA 02138

#57
Inman Square
Landmark/Historical
Area: Inman Square
Address: Cambridge & Hampshire St
Cambridge, MA 02139

#58
Prospect Hill Monument
Landmark/Historical
Address: Munroe St at Bigelow St
Somerville, MA 02143

#59
**Chinese Historical Society
of New England**
Landmark/Historical
Area: Chinatown
Address: 2 Boylston St
Boston, MA 02116
Phone: (617) 338-4339

#60
**Boston Historical Society
and Museum**
Landmark/Historical
Area: Downtown
Address: 206 Washington St
Boston, MA 02109
Phone: (617) 720-1713

#61
JFK Birthplace
Landmark/Historical
Address: 83 Beals St
Brookline, MA 02445

#62
30 Federal St Bldg
Landmark/Historical
Area: Financial District
Address: 30 Federal St Fl 6
Boston, MA 02110
Phone: (617) 426-8283

#63
Weeks Footbridge
Landmark/Historical
Area: Harvard Square
Address: 953 Memorial Dr
Cambridge, MA 02138

#64
Battle of Bunker Hill Museum
Tour, Museum,
Landmark/Historical
Area: Charlestown
Address: 43 Monument Sq
Charlestown, MA 02129
Phone: (617) 242-7275

#65
Madonna Queen National Shrine
Landmark/Historical
Area: East Boston
Address: 111 Orient ave East
Boston, MA 02128
Phone: (617) 569-2100

#66
Fort Washington
Landmark/Historical, Park
Area: Kendall Square
Address: 115 Waverly St
Cambridge, MA 02139

#67
Carpenter Center for the Visual Arts
Landmark/Historical
Area: Harvard Square
Address: 24 Quincy Street
Cambridge, MA 02138

#68
Highland Park - Fort Hill
Landmark/Historical, Park
Address: 20 Fort Ave
Roxbury, MA 02119

#69
Adams National Historical Park
Park, Landmark/Historical
Address: 1250 Hancock St
Quincy, MA 02169

#70
**Government Center
MBTA Station**
Landmark/Historical,
Public Transportation
Area: Downtown
Address: Tremont & Court St
Intersection Boston, MA 02108

#71
Washington Tower
Landmark/Historical
Area: Harvard Square
Address: 580 Mount Auburn Street
Cambridge, MA 02138

#72
Soldiers Monument
Landmark/Historical,
Area: Jamaica Plain
Address: Centre and South Sts
Jamaica Plain, MA 02130

#73
Beaver Brook Reservation
Landmark/Historical, Park
Address: 66 Mill St
Belmont, MA 02478

#74
Wellington Bridge
Landmark/Historical
Address: Fellsway Medford, MA

#75
Secret Squantum Park
Landmark/Historical, Park
Address: 20 Moon Island Rd
North Quincy, MA 02171

#76
Dorchester Historical Society
Landmark/Historical
Area: Dorchester
Address: 195 Boston St
Dorchester, MA 02125
Phone: (617) 265-7802

#77
Quincy Historical Society
Landmark/Historical
Address: 8 Adams Street
Quincy, MA 02169

#78
Rivercourt Condominiums
Landmark/Historical
Area: East Cambridge
Address: 10 Rogers St
Cambridge, MA 02142
Phone: (617) 494-8844

#79
Olmstead Historic Site
Landmark/Historical
Address: 99 Warren St
Brookline, MA 02445

#80
Historic Hyde Square
Landmark/Historical
Area: Jamaica Plain
Address: 59 Round Hill St
Jamaica Plain, MA 02130
Phone: (800) 983-1894

#81
Simmons Hall
Landmark/Historical
Area: Kendall Square/MIT
Address: 229 Vassar St
Cambridge, MA 02139

#82
The James Kelly Bridge
Landmark/Historical
Area: South Boston
Address: The James Kelly Bridge South
Boston, MA 02127

#83
One Kendall Square
Landmark/Historical,
Shopping, Restaurant
Area: Kendall Square/MIT
Address: Hampshire St & Broadway St
Cambridge, MA 02139

#84
Grape Island
Landmark/Historical
Address: Boston Harbor Islands
Harbor Islands, MA 02169

#85
Reid Overpass
Landmark/Historical, Transportation
Area: Kendall Square/MIT
Address: 642 Memorial Dr
Cambridge, MA 02139

#86
Saugus Iron Works
Landmark/Historical, Museum
Address: 244 Central St
Saugus, MA 01906

#87
Strauss Trunnion Bascule Bridge
Landmark/Historical
Area: East Cambridge
Address: 1st St and Land Blvd
Cambridge, MA 02142

#88
Fort Revere Park
Park, Landmark/Historical
Address: 60 Farina Rd
Hull, MA 02045

#89
Lyman Estate
Landmark/Historical,
Venues, Event Space
Address: 185 Lyman St
Waltham, MA 02452

#90
Town Hall of Winchester
Landmark/Historical, Notaries
Address: 71 Mt. Vernon St
Winchester, MA 01890

#91
South End Historical Society Inc
Landmark/Historical
Area: South End
Address: 532 Massachusetts Ave
Roxbury, MA 02118
Phone: (617) 536-4445

#92
Dorchester Historical Society
Landmark/Historical
Area: Dorchester
Address: 199 Boston St
Dorchester, MA 02125
Phone: (617) 436-1492

#93
Eastern National
Landmark/Historical
Area: Charlestown
Address: 43 Monument Sq
Charlestown, MA 02129
Phone: (617) 242-0347

#94
Shipyard Quarters Marina
Landmark/Historical
Area: Charlestown
Address: Charlestown Navy Yd
Charlestown, MA 02129
Phone: (617) 242-2020

#95
**United First Parish Church
Unitarian**
Landmark/Historical, Church
Address: 1306 Hancock St
Quincy, MA 02169

#96
Lexington Battle Green
Landmark/Historical
Address: Massachusetts Ave &
Bedford St Lexington, MA 02420

#97
Melrose Memorial Hall
Landmark/Historical
Address: 590 Main St
Melrose, MA 02176

#98
**Blue Hill Observatory
Science Center**
Landmark/Historical
Address: 1904 Canton Ave
Milton, MA 02186

#99
Stonehurst
Landmark/Historical, Museum
Address: 100 Robert Treat Paine Dr
Waltham, MA 02452

#100
Robert Treat Paine Estate
Landmark/Historical, Museum
Address: 100 Robert Treat Pane Dr
Waltham, MA 02452

TOP 400 ENTERTAINMENT

Most Recommended by Locals & Trevelers
Ranking (from #1 to #400)

#1
Fenway Park
Category: Stadium/Arena
Area: Fenway
Address: 4 Yawkey Way
Boston, MA 02115
Phone: (877) 733-7699

#2
Wine Riot
Category: Festival
Area: Back Bay
Address: 130 Columbus Ave
Boston, MA 02116

#3
Museum Of Fine Arts
Category: Museum, Art Gallery
Average price: Modest
Area: Phone number
Address: 465 Huntington Ave
Boston, MA 02115

#4
Boston Opera House
Category: Performing Arts
Area: Downtown
Address: 539 Washington St
Boston, MA 02108
Phone: (617) 259-3400

#5
Isabella Stewart Gardner Museum
Category: Museum
Area: Phone number
Address: 280 The Fenway
Boston, MA 02115

#6
Improv Asylum
Category: Comedy Club
Average price: Modest
Area: North End
Address: 216 Hanover St
Boston, MA 02113
Phone: (617) 263-6887

#7
John F Kennedy Presidential Library & Museum
Category: Museum
Area: Dorchester
Address: 220 Morrissey Blvd
Boston, MA 02125
Phone: (617) 514-1600

#8
Museum of Science
Category: Museum, Cinema
Area: East Cambridge
Address: 1 Science Park
Boston, MA 02114
Phone: (617) 723-2500

#9
Boston Children's Museum
Category: Museum
Area: Waterfront, South Boston
Address: 308 Congress St
Boston, MA 02210
Phone: (617) 426-6500

#10
Shakespeare on the Common
Category: Park, Performing Arts
Area: Back Bay
Address: Boston Common
Boston, MA 02116
Phone: (617) 426-0863

#11
Bank Of America Pavilion
Category: Stadium/Arena,
Music Venues
Average price: Expensive
Area: Waterfront, South Boston
Address: 290 Northern Ave
Boston, MA 02210
Phone: (800) 653-8000

#12
The Beehive
Category: Jazz & Blues, American,
Breakfast & Brunch
Average price: Expensive
Area: South End
Address: 541 Tremont St
Boston, MA 02116
Phone: (617) 423-0069

#13
Boston Wine School
Category: Venues, Event Space, Winery,
Specialty School
Average price: Modest
Area: Allston/Brighton
Address: 1354 Commonwealth Ave
Boston, MA 02134
Phone: (617) 784-7150

#14
The Urban Art Bar
Category: Arts & Entertainment,
Venues, Event Space
Area: South Boston
Address: 163 Old Colony Ave
Boston, MA 02127
Phone: (617) 596-0553

#15
The Lyric Stage Company of Boston
Category: Performing Arts
Area: Back Bay
Address: 140 Clarendon St
Boston, MA 02116
Phone: (617) 585-5678

#16
Institute of Contemporary Art
Category: Museum
Area: Waterfront, South Boston
Address: 100 Northern Ave
Boston, MA 02210
Phone: (617) 478-3100

#17
Cyclorama at Boston Center for the Arts
Category: Venues, Event Space,
Performing Arts
Area: South End
Address: 539 Tremont St
Boston, MA 02116
Phone: (617) 426-5000

#18
Boston Ballet
Category: Performing Arts,
Dance School, Opera & Ballet
Area: South End
Address: 19 Clarendon St
Boston, MA 02116
Phone: (617) 695-6955

#19
Simons IMAX Theatre
Category: Cinema
Area: Chinatown
Address: 1 Central Wharf
Boston, MA 02111
Phone: (866) 815-4629

#20
Boston Winery
Category: Winery
Average price: Inexpensive
Area: Dorchester
Address: 26 Ericsson St
Boston, MA 02122
Phone: (617) 265-9463

#21
Boston Celtics
Category: Professional Sports Team
Area: North End
Address: 100 Legends Way
Boston, MA 02114
Phone: (617) 854-8000

#22
Artists For Humanity Epicenter
Category: Venues, Event Space,
Art Gallery
Average price: Modest
Area: South Boston
Address: 100 West Second St
Boston, MA 02127
Phone: (617) 268-7620

#23
Boston Center for the Arts
Category: Art Gallery, Performing Arts,
Venues, Event Space
Average price: Modest
Area: South End
Address: 539 Tremont St
Boston, MA 02116
Phone: (617) 426-5000

#24
Old South Meeting House
Category: Museum
Area: Beacon Hill
Address: 310 Washington St
Boston, MA 02108
Phone: (617) 482-6439

#25
Gibson House Museum
Category: Museum
Area: Back Bay
Address: 137 Beacon St
Boston, MA 02116
Phone: (617) 267-6338

#26
Old State House
Category: Museum, Landmark/Historical
Area: Downtown
Address: 206 Washington St
Boston, MA 02108
Phone: (617) 720-1713

#27
Regal Fenway Stadium 13
Category: Cinema
Area: Fenway
Address: 201 Brookline Ave
Boston, MA 02215
Phone: (617) 424-6111

#28
Boston Wine Expo
Category: Winery, Beer, Wine, Spirits
Average price: Expensive
Area: Waterfront, South Boston
Address: 200 Seaport Blvd
Boston, MA 02210
Phone: (877) 946-3976

#29
SOWA Artists Guild
Category: Art Gallery
Average price: Modest
Area: South End
Address: 450 Harrison Ave
Boston, MA 02228
Phone: (978) 337-4191

#30
Society of Arts, Crafts
Category: Arts, Crafts, Art Gallery
Average price: Modest
Area: Back Bay
Address: 175 Newbury St
Boston, MA 02116
Phone: (617) 266-1810

#31
Around the Corner
Category: Framing, Art Gallery
Average price: Expensive
Area: South End
Address: 637 Tremont St
Boston, MA 02118
Phone: (617) 266-1800

#32
Ars Libri
Category: Art Gallery, Bookstore
Average price: Modest
Area: South End
Address: 500 Harrison Ave
Boston, MA 02118
Phone: (617) 357-5212

#33
The Red Room @ Cafe 939
Category: Coffee & Tea, Music Venues
Average price: Inexpensive
Area: Back Bay
Address: 939 Boylston St
Boston, MA 02115
Phone: (617) 747-2261

#34
Howl At The Moon Dueling
Piano Bar
Category: Bar, Music Venues
Average price: Modest
Area: Financial District
Address: 184 High St
Boston, MA 02110
Phone: (617) 292-4695

#35
Nichols House Museum
Category: Museum
Area: Beacon Hill
Address: 55 Mount Vernon St
Boston, MA 02108
Phone: (617) 227-6993

#36
Boston Tea Party Ships & Museum
Category: Museum
Area: Waterfront, South Boston
Address: 306 Congress St
Boston, MA 02109
Phone: (617) 338-1773

#37
The Paul Revere House
Category: Museum
Area: North End
Address: 19 N Sq
Boston, MA 02113
Phone: (617) 523-2338

#38
StyleFixx
Category: Festival
Area: South End
Address: 539 Tremont St
Boston, MA 02116
Phone: (617) 719-9999

#39
Eugene Gallery
Category: Art Gallery
Average price: Expensive
Area: Beacon Hill
Address: 76 Charles St
Boston, MA 02114
Phone: (617) 227-3062

#40
House Of Blues Boston
Category: Venues, Event Space,
Jazz & Blues
Average price: Modest
Area: Fenway
Address: 15 Lansdowne St
Boston, MA 02215
Phone: (800) 653-8000

#41
Photographic Resource Center
Category: Art Gallery
Average price: Inexpensive
Area: Allston/Brighton
Address: 832 Commonwealth Ave
Boston, MA 02215
Phone: (617) 975-0600

#42
Boston Gay Mens Chorus
Category: Performing Arts
Area: South End
Address: 95 Berkeley St
Boston, MA 02116
Phone: (617) 542-7464

#43
Bill's Bar & Lounge
Category: Sports Bar, Music Venues
Average price: Modest
Area: Fenway
Address: 5 Lansdowne St
Boston, MA 02215
Phone: (617) 247-1222

#44
Fort Point Framers
Category: Art Gallery, Framing
Area: Waterfront, South Boston
Address: 300 Summer St
Boston, MA 02210
Phone: (617) 482-4685

#45
Boston Symphony Orchestra
Category: Performing Arts
Area: Fenway
Address: 930 Commonwealth Ave
Boston, MA 02215
Phone: (413) 637-1666

#46
Orpheum Theatre
Category: Music Venues
Average price: Modest
Area: Downtown
Address: 1 Hamilton Pl
Boston, MA 02108
Phone: (617) 482-0106

#47
Boston Babydolls Burlesque
Category: Performing Arts,
Specialty School
Area: Allston/Brighton
Address: 119 Braintree St
Boston, MA 02134
Phone: (617) 869-2000

#48
SpeakEasy Stage Company
Category: Performing Arts
Area: South End
Address: 539 Tremont St
Boston, MA 02116
Phone: (617) 482-3279

#49
Mayan Weavers
Category: Arts, Crafts, Art Gallery
Average price: Modest
Area: Back Bay
Address: 268 Newbury St
Boston, MA 02116
Phone: (617) 262-4342

#50
Boston Breakers
Category: Professional Sports Team
Area: Allston/Brighton
Address: 95 North Harvard St
Boston, MA 02134
Phone: (877) 439-2732

#51
**Museum of African
American History**
Category: Museum, Tour
Area: Beacon Hill
Address: 46 Joy St
Boston, MA 02108
Phone: (617) 725-0022

#52
BosTix
Category: Ticket Sale
Area: Back Bay
Address: 650A Boylston St
Boston, MA 02116
Phone: (617) 262-8632

#53
**Girl Scouts of Eastern
Massachusetts**
Category: Social Club
Area: South End
Address: 95 Berkeley St
Boston, MA 02116
Phone: (617) 482-1078

#54
Lasker's
Category: Social Club
Area: South End
Address: 67 Appleton Street
Boston, MA 02116
Phone: (617) 482-2638

#55
Company One
Category: Performing Arts, Education
Area: South End
Address: 539 Tremont St
Boston, MA 02116
Phone: (617) 292-7110

#56
DTR Modern Gallery
Category: Art Gallery
Average price: Exclusive
Area: Back Bay
Address: 167 Newbury St
Boston, MA 02116
Phone: (617) 424-9700

#57
Galeria Cubana
Category: Art Gallery
Area: South End
Address: 460 Harrison Ave
Boston, MA 02118
Phone: (617) 292-2822

#58
Tremont Tearoom
Category: Psychic, Astrologer
Area: Downtown
Address: 101 Tremont St
Boston, MA 02108
Phone: (617) 338-8100

#59
Bright Hockey Center
Category: Stadium/Arena
Area: Allston/Brighton
Address: 65 N Harvard St
Boston, MA 02134
Phone: (617) 495-2211

#60
Calderwood Pavilion
Category: Performing Arts,
Venues, Event Space
Area: South End
Address: 527 Tremont St
Boston, MA 02115
Phone: (617) 933-8600

#61
The Picture Store
Category: Art Gallery, Framing
Average price: Exclusive
Area: South End
Address: 65 Berkeley St
Boston, MA 02116
Phone: (617) 426-5144

#62
**Community Music
Center of Boston**
Category: Music Venues
Area: South End
Address: 34 Warren Ave
Boston, MA 02116
Phone: (617) 482-7494

#63
AIC Boston Center
Category: Venues, Event Space,
Music Venues, Art Gallery
Average price: Modest
Area: Back Bay
Address: 38 Newbury St
Boston, MA 02116
Phone: (617) 266-0080

#64
Lanoue Fine Art
Category: Art Gallery
Area: Back Bay
Address: 125 Newbury Street
Boston, MA 02116
Phone: (617) 262-4400

#65
Gallery Kayafas
Category: Art Gallery
Average price: Expensive
Area: South End
Address: 450 Harrison Ave
Boston, MA 02118
Phone: (617) 482-0411

#66
Goosefish Press
Category: Art Gallery
Area: South End
Address: 450 Harrison Ave
Boston, MA 02127
Phone: (617) 728-2822

#67
Samsøn
Category: Art Gallery
Average price: Expensive
Area: South End
Address: 450 Harrison Ave
Boston, MA 02118
Phone: (617) 357-7177

#68
Zeitgeist Stage Company
Category: Performing Arts
Area: South End
Address: 116 W Newton St
Boston, MA 02118
Phone: (617) 759-8836

#69
Vose Gallery of Boston
Category: Antiques, Art Gallery
Area: Back Bay
Address: 238 Newbury St
Boston, MA 02116
Phone: (617) 536-6176

#70
East Coast Soul
Category: Performing Arts, Musicians
Area: South End
Address: 580 Harrison Ave
Boston, MA 02118
Phone: (617) 901-5609

#71
Boston Guitar Repair Center
Category: Musical Instruments,
Performing Arts, Specialty School
Average price: Modest
Address: 131 W Concord St
Boston, MA 02118
Phone: (857) 207-2248

#72
Publick Theatre
Category: Performing Arts
Area: Allston/Brighton
Address: 398 Columbus Ave
Boston, MA 02116
Phone: (617) 454-1444

#73
Lannan Ship Model Gallery
Category: Antiques, Art Gallery
Average price: Expensive
Area: Financial District
Address: 99 High Street
Boston, MA 02110
Phone: (617) 451-2650

#74
Boston Fun Cruises
Category: Tour, Jazz & Blues
Average price: Inexpensive
Area: Waterfront, South Boston
Address: 88 Sleeper St
Boston, MA 02210
Phone: (617) 821-6127

#75
Gold Dust Orphans
Category: Performing Arts
Area: Back Bay
Address: 254 Boylston St
Boston, MA 02116
Phone: (617) 265-6222

#76
Sirry Berndsen
Category: Psychic, Astrologer
Area: Jamaica Plain
Address: 82 South St
Boston, MA 02130
Phone: (617) 262-2080

#77
**Copperfield's Bar
& Down Under Pub**
Category: Bar, Music Venues
Average price: Modest
Area: Fenway
Address: 98 Brookline Ave
Boston, MA 02215
Phone: (617) 247-8605

#78
Ace Ticket Agency
Category: Arts & Entertainment
Area: Fenway
Address: 121 Brookline Ave
Boston, MA 02215
Phone: (617) 783-3333

#79
Back Bay Events Center
Category: Performing Arts,
Music Venues
Area: Back Bay
Address: 180 Berkeley St
Boston, MA 02116
Phone: (617) 236-1199

#80
Pucker Gallery
Category: Art Gallery
Area: Back Bay
Address: 171 Newbury St
Boston, MA 02116
Phone: (617) 267-9473

#81
Carroll & Sons Gallery
Category: Art Gallery
Average price: Expensive
Area: South End
Address: 450 Harrison Ave
Boston, MA 02118
Phone: (617) 482-2477

#82
Boston Fire Museum
Category: Museum
Area: Waterfront, South Boston
Address: 344 Congress St
Boston, MA 02210
Phone: (617) 482-1344

#83
The Backbay Framery
Category: Art Gallery, Framing
Average price: Modest
Area: Back Bay
Address: 227 Newbury St
Boston, MA 02116
Phone: (617) 424-1550

#84
**ArtsEmerson:
The World On Stage**
Category: Performing Arts
Area: Chinatown
Address: 559 Washington St
Boston, MA 02111
Phone: (617) 824-8000

#85
Mystery Cafe Dinner Theater
Category: Performing Arts,
Party & Event Planning
Average price: Expensive
Area: Financial District
Address: 161 Devonshire St
Boston, MA 02110
Phone: (781) 784-7469

#86
Boston Local Food Festival
Category: Festival
Area: Waterfront, South Boston
Address: The Greenway
Boston, MA 02210
Phone: (617) 575-9165

#87
The Vilna Shul
Category: Museum
Area: Beacon Hill
Address: 18 Phillips St
Boston, MA 02114
Phone: (617) 523-2324

#88
Matrix
Category: Dance Club, Music Venues
Area: Back Bay
Address: 275 Tremont St
Boston, MA 02116
Phone: (617) 542-4077

#89
Laugh Boston
Category: Performing Arts, Comedy Club
Average price: Modest
Area: South Boston
Address: 425 Summer St
Boston, MA 02210
Phone: (617) 725-2844

#90
First Night
Category: Performing Arts
Area: Back Bay
Address: 36 Bromfield St
Boston, MA 02116
Phone: (617) 542-1399

#91
**Mills Gallery at Boston
Center for the Arts**
Category: Art Gallery, Performing Arts
Area: South End
Address: 539 Tremont St
Boston, MA 02116
Phone: (617) 426-8835

#92
**Plaza Theatres at Boston
Center for the Arts**
Category: Performing Arts, Music Venues
Area: South End
Address: 539 Tremont St
Boston, MA 02116
Phone: (617) 426-5000

#93
The Copley Society of Art
Category: Art Gallery
Area: Back Bay
Address: 158 Newbury St
Boston, MA 02116
Phone: (617) 536-5049

#94
Howard Yezerski Gallery
Category: Art Gallery
Average price: Exclusive
Area: South End
Address: 460 Harrison Ave
Boston, MA 02118
Phone: (617) 262-0550

#95
Dick Doherty's Comedy Den
Category: Comedy Club
Average price: Modest
Area: Financial District
Address: 184 High St
Boston, MA 02110
Phone: (800) 401-2221

#96
Ione Face Painting
Category: Performing Arts,
Makeup Artists
Area: South End
Address: 106 Chandler St
Boston, MA 02116
Phone: (617) 785-7523

#97
Vagabond Theatre Group
Category: Performing Arts
Area: South End
Address: 539 Tremont St
Boston, MA 02116
Phone: (617) 383-9517

#98
Barbara Krakow Gallery
Category: Art Gallery
Area: Back Bay
Address: 10 Newbury St
Boston, MA 02116
Phone: (617) 262-4490

#99
Emmanuel Music
Category: Performing Arts
Area: Back Bay
Address: 15 Newbury St
Boston, MA 02116
Phone: (617) 536-3356

#100
Martin Lawrence Art Gallery
Category: Art Gallery
Area: Back Bay
Address: 77 Newbury St
Boston, MA 02116
Phone: (617) 369-4800

#101
Guild of Boston Artists
Category: Art Gallery
Area: Back Bay
Address: 162 Newbury Street
Boston, MA 02116
Phone: (617) 536-7660

#102
Chase Young Gallery
Category: Art Gallery
Area: South End
Address: 450 Harrison Ave
Boston, MA 02118
Phone: (617) 859-7222

#103
Night Shift Entertainment
Category: Performing Arts
Area: South End
Address: 580 Harrison Ave
Boston, MA 02118
Phone: (857) 250-2064

#104
One Love Entertainment
Category: Performing Arts
Area: Back Bay
Address: 254 Commonwealth Ave
Boston, MA 02115
Phone: (617) 504-5943

#105
Madman with a Marker
Category: Performing Arts
Area: Beacon Hill
Address: 1 Faneuil Hall
Boston, MA 02108
Phone: (978) 327-9957

#106
Sloane Merrill Gallery
Category: Art Gallery
Area: Beacon Hill
Address: 75 Charles St
Boston, MA 02114
Phone: (617) 227-1775

#107
Alberts-Langdon
Category: Art Gallery, Antiques
Area: Beacon Hill
Address: 126 Charles St
Boston, MA 02114
Phone: (617) 523-5954

#108
New Center For Arts & Culture
Category: Museum
Area: Beacon Hill
Address: 18 Tremont St
Boston, MA 02108
Phone: (617) 531-4610

#109
StageSource
Category: Performing Arts
Area: Beacon Hill
Address: 88 Tremont St
Boston, MA 02108
Phone: (617) 720-6066

#110
Studio Soto
Category: Art Gallery
Area: South Boston
Address: 10 Channel Center St
Boston, MA 02210
Phone: (617) 426-7686

#111
The Sports Museum
Category: Museum
Area: Downtown
Address: 100 Legends Way
Boston, MA 02114
Phone: (617) 624-1234

#112
Boston Flower & Garden Show
Category: Botanical Garden
Area: Waterfront, South Boston
Address: 200 Seaport Blvd
Boston, MA 02210
Phone: (617) 385-5000

#113
Boston Harborfest
Category: Arts & Entertainment
Area: Downtown
Address: 45 School Street
Boston, MA 02108
Phone: (617) 227-1528

#114
The Stupendous Mr. Magichead
Category: Performing Arts, Magicians
Area: South Boston
Address: 343 West Broadway St
Boston, MA 02127
Phone: (508) 450-7110

#115
Ancient and Honorable Artillery Company
Category: Museum
Area: North End
Address: Faneuil Hall Marketplace
Boston, MA 02109
Phone: (617) 227-1638

#116
Greater Boston House Concerts
Category: Music Venues
Area: Dorchester
Address: 21 Virginia St
Boston, MA 02125
Phone: (617) 947-1330

#117
Cochon555
Category: Ticket Sale
Area: Allston/Brighton
Address: 967 Commonwealth Ave
Boston, MA 02215
Phone: (678) 744-5886

#118
Commonwealth Museum
Category: Museum
Area: Dorchester
Address: 220 Morrissey Blvd
Boston, MA 02125
Phone: (617) 727-9268

#119
Church
Category: American, Music Venues
Average price: Modest
Area: Fenway
Address: 69 Kilmarnock St
Boston, MA 02215
Phone: (617) 236-7600

#120
Copley Art & Framing
Category: Art Gallery, Framing
Average price: Expensive
Area: Back Bay
Address: 150 Huntington Ave
Boston, MA 02115
Phone: (617) 267-6060

#121
Massmouth
Category: Performing Arts
Area: Jamaica Plain
Address: 42 Seaverns Ave
Boston, MA 02130
Phone: (617) 942-2553

#122
Media Performance Institute
Category: Art School, Performing Arts
Area: Allston/Brighton
Address: 129 Braintree St
Boston, MA 02134
Phone: (617) 254-1001

#123
**New England International
Auto Show**
Category: Entertainment, Automotive
Area: South Boston
Address: 415 Summer St
Boston, MA 02210
Phone: (781) 237-5533

#124
**T. Benjamin Fiske Custom
Framing & Fine Art**
Category: Art Gallery, Framing
Area: Dorchester
Address: 1162 Washington St
Boston, MA 02124
Phone: (617) 298-1837

#125
Garacci Group
Category: Performing Arts
Area: Fenway
Address: 25 Peterborough St
Boston, MA 02215
Phone: (857) 891-3222

#126
**Noa Jewelry, Fine
Handcrafts & Gifts**
Category: Jewelry, Art Gallery
Average price: Expensive
Area: Beacon Hill
Address: 88 Charles St
Boston, MA 02114
Phone: (857) 233-4912

#127
International Poster Gallery
Category: Art Gallery
Average price: Expensive
Area: Back Bay
Address: 205 Newbury St
Boston, MA 02116
Phone: (617) 375-0076

#128
The Dinner Detective
Category: American, Performing Arts
Area: Back Bay
Address: 140 Clarendon St
Boston, MA 02116
Phone: (888) 573-4401

#129
Gallery NAGA
Category: Art Gallery
Area: Back Bay
Address: 67 Newbury St
Boston, MA 02116
Phone: (617) 267-9060

#130
Kidder Smith Gallery
Category: Art Gallery
Area: Back Bay
Address: 131 Newbury St
Boston, MA 02116
Phone: (617) 424-6900

#131
Roessler Glass
Category: Jewelry, Art Gallery
Area: South End
Address: 46 Waltham
Boston, MA 02118
Phone: (617) 268-0600

#132
Fort Point Arts Community
Category: Art Gallery
Average price: Inexpensive
Area: Waterfront, South Boston
Address: 300 Summer Street
Boston, MA 02210
Phone: (617) 423-4299

#133
Rock On
Category: Music Venues, Bar
Area: Waterfront
Address: 60 Rowes Wharf
Boston, MA 02110
Phone: (617) 544-7625

#134
Rock On! Concert Cruises
Category: Music Venues
Area: Waterfront
Address: 60 Rowes Wharf
Boston, MA 02210
Phone: (617) 544-7625

#135
Shake the Tree Gallery
Category: Art Gallery
Area: North End
Address: 67 Salem St
Boston, MA 02113
Phone: (617) 742-0484

#136
AfterHours
Category: Music Venues
Average price: Inexpensive
Area: Fenway
Address: 360 Huntington Avenue
Boston, MA 02115
Phone: (617) 373-2642

#137
Paul Revere House the
Category: Museum
Area: South Boston
Address: 19 N St
Boston, MA 02127
Phone: (617) 523-2338

#138
Boston Playwrights' Theatre
Category: Performing Arts
Area: Allston/Brighton
Address: 949 Commonwealth Ave
Boston, MA 02215
Phone: (617) 353-5443

#139
Walter Brown Arena
Category: Stadium/Arena
Area: Allston/Brighton
Address: 285 Babcock Street
Boston, MA 02215
Phone: (617) 353-4632

#140
CraftBoston Spring
Category: Festival, Arts, Crafts
Average price: Expensive
Area: South End
Address: 539 Tremont St
Boston, MA 02116
Phone: (617) 266-1810

#141
Boston's Best Psychic
Category: Party & Event Planning,
Psychic, Astrologer, Life Coach
Area: Back Bay
Address: 0 Beacon St
Boston, MA 02116
Phone: (617) 942-0689

#142
Pandemonium
Category: Event Planning,
Service, Performing Arts
Area: Jamaica Plain
Address: Hank Agency
Boston, MA 02130
Phone: (617) 628-0400

#143
Boston Lyric Opera
Category: Performing Arts
Area: Downtown
Address: 45 Franklin St
Boston, MA 02110
Phone: (617) 542-4912

#144
Fishnet Networks
Category: Performing Arts
Area: Back Bay
Address: 209 Columbus Ave
Boston, MA 02116
Phone: (781) 249-4681

#145
Boston Artwork
Category: Art Gallery
Area: Back Bay
Address: 800 Boylston St.
Boston, MA 02199
Phone: (617) 472-1695

#146
Johnson Artist Materials
Category: Art Supplies, Art Gallery
Average price: Modest
Area: Back Bay
Address: 355 Newbury St
Boston, MA 02115
Phone: (617) 536-4065

#147
Made in Fort Point
Category: Arts, Crafts, Art Gallery
Area: South Boston
Address: 30 Channel Ctr St
Boston, MA 02210
Phone: (617) 423-1100

#148
Remis Auditorium
Category: Performing Arts
Area: Fenway
Address: 465 Huntington Ave
Boston, MA 02115
Phone: (617) 369-3300

#149
BU Central
Category: Music Venues
Area: Allston/Brighton
Address: 775 Commonwealth Ave
Boston, MA 02215
Phone: (617) 353-3635

#150
Shecky's Girls Night Out
Category: Festival
Area: Back Bay
Address: 130 Columbus Ave
Boston, MA 02116
Phone: (617) 426-2000

#151
Lavietes Pavilion
Category: Stadium/Arena
Area: Allston/Brighton
Address: Harvard University
Boston, MA 02163
Phone: (617) 495-2211

#152
JRP New England
Category: Performing Arts
Area: Financial District
Address: 211 Congress St
Boston, MA 02110
Phone: (617) 946-0508

#153
Agganis Arena
Category: Stadium/Arena
Area: Allston/Brighton
Address: 925 Commonwealth Ave
Boston, MA 02215
Phone: (617) 358-7000

#154
Down-4-Life
Category: Arts & Entertainment
Area: Downtown
Address: Boston, MA 02112
Phone: (774) 244-2476

#155
Kingston Gallery
Category: Art Gallery
Area: South End
Address: 450 Harrison Ave
Boston, MA 02118
Phone: (617) 423-4113

#156
**Selena's New Age
Psychic Shop**
Category: Psychic, Astrologer
Area: South End
Address: 678 Tremont Street
Boston, MA 02228
Phone: (617) 267-1077

#157
The Childrens Museum
Category: Museum
Area: Waterfront, South Boston
Address: 308 Congress St
Boston, MA 02210
Phone: (617) 426-6500

#158
Galerie d'Orsay
Category: Art Gallery
Average price: Exclusive
Area: Back Bay
Address: 33 Newbury Street
Boston, MA 02116
Phone: (617) 266-8001

#159
Telebelles Singing Telegrams
Category: Arts & Entertainment
Area: South Boston
Address: 25 Drydock Ave
Boston, MA 02210
Phone: (617) 464-1212

#160
Axelle Fine Arts Galerie
Area: Back Bay
Address: 91 Newbury St
Boston, MA 02116
Phone: (617) 450-0700

#161
Psychic Lauren
Area: Back Bay
Address: 216 Newbury St
Boston, MA 02116
Phone: (617) 784-4192

#162
Exclusive Jewels
Category: Jewelry, Bridal, Art Gallery
Area: Beacon Hill
Address: 121 Charles St
Boston, MA 02114
Phone: (617) 367-8181

#163
Ford Hall Forum
at Suffolk University
Area: Beacon Hill
Address: 41 Temple St
Boston, MA 02114
Phone: (617) 557-2007

#164
Jazz In The Air
Category: Musicians, Jazz & Blues
Area: Fenway
Address: St Marys St
Boston, MA 02115
Phone: (978) 898-4975

#165
Boston Children's Theatre
Category: Performing Arts
Area: Fenway
Address: 316 Huntington Ave
Boston, MA 02115
Phone: (617) 424-6634

#166
Superstition
Area: Fenway
Address: 835 Beacon St
Boston, MA 02215
Phone: (617) 262-2121

#167
hancock tower
Area: Back Bay
Address: 1,Ecke Trinity Place
und St.James Ave.
Boston, MA 02116
Phone: (617) 247-1977

#168
Pro Arte Chamber
Orchestra of Boston
Area: Back Bay
Address: 75 Arlington St
Boston, MA 02116
Phone: (617) 779-0900

#169
Boston International
Fine Art Show
Area: South End
Address: 539 Tremont St
Boston, MA 02116
Phone: (617) 363-0405

#170
Quidley & Company
Area: Back Bay
Address: 38 Newbury St
Boston, MA 02116
Phone: (617) 450-4300

#171
Newbury Fine Arts
Area: Back Bay
Address: 29 Newbury St
Boston, MA 02116
Phone: (617) 536-0210

#172
Iris Gallery of Fine Art
Area: Back Bay
Address: 129 Newbury St
Boston, MA 02116
Phone: (617) 585-1010

#173
Oliver Brothers
Area: Back Bay
Address: 162 Newbury St
Boston, MA 02116
Phone: (617) 536-2323

#174
Vessels Gallery
Area: South End
Address: 450 Harrison Ave
Boston, MA 02118
Phone: (617) 426-1950

#175
Boston Sculptors Gallery
Area: South End
Address: 486 Harrison Ave
Boston, MA 02118
Phone: (617) 482-7781

#176
L'Attitude Gallery
Area: Back Bay
Address: 211 Newbury St
Boston, MA 02116
Phone: (617) 927-4400

#177
Spiritual Readings by Adriana
Area: Back Bay
Address: Boylston St
Boston, MA 02199
Phone: (617) 999-2560

#178
Modern Theatre
Category: Performing Arts
Area: Downtown
Address: 525 Washington St
Boston, MA 02111
Phone: (617) 557-6537

#179
Psychic Readings by Hanna
Area: North End
Address: 215 Hanover St
Boston, MA 02113
Phone: (617) 910-6587

#180
Fenway Ticket King
Category: Ticket Sale
Area: Fenway
Address: 4 Yawkey Way
Boston, MA 02215
Phone: (877) 870-3649

#181
Studio 52
Category: Performing Arts,
Recording & Rehearsal Studio
Area: Allston/Brighton
Address: 52 Everett St
Boston, MA 02134
Phone: (617) 783-5252

#182
**AD20/21: Art & Design
of the 20th & 21st Centuries**
Area: South End
Address: 539 Tremont St
Boston, MA 02116
Phone: (617) 363-0405

#183
Ellis Boston Antiques Show
Area: South End
Address: 539 Tremont St
Boston, MA 02116
Phone: (617) 363-0405

#184
Celebrity Series of Boston
Area: Back Bay
Address: 20 Park Plz
Boston, MA 02116
Phone: (617) 482-2595

#185
Alpha Gallery Inc
Area: Back Bay
Address: 37 Newbury St
Boston, MA 02116
Phone: (617) 536-4465

#186
Copley Society of Boston
Area: Back Bay
Address: 158 Newbury St
Boston, MA 02116
Phone: (617) 536-2787

#187
Gold Gallery
Area: South End
Address: 655 Tremont St
Boston, MA 02118
Phone: (857) 239-8972

#188
Nielsen Gallery
Area: Back Bay
Address: 179 Newbury St
Boston, MA 02116
Phone: (617) 266-4835

#189
Gurari Collections
Area: South End
Address: 460 Harrison Ave
Boston, MA 02118
Phone: (617) 367-9800

#190
Cantata Singers
Area: Back Bay
Address: 729 Boylston St
Boston, MA 02116
Phone: (617) 868-5885

#191
B Glee Lucas Fine Arts
Area: South End
Address: 450 Harrison Ave
Boston, MA 02118
Phone: (617) 869-5349

#192
Guilded Boston
Area: Back Bay
Address: 213 Newbury Street
Boston, MA 02116
Phone: (617) 429-8968

#193
**Four-Handed Illusions: An Intimate
Evening of Laughs and Wonder**
Category: Comedy Club
Average price: Modest
Area: Beacon Hill
Address: 84 Beacon St
Boston, MA 02108
Phone: (781) 850-6924

#194
Paramount Center
Area: Chinatown
Address: 559 Washington St
Boston, MA 02111
Phone: (617) 824-8000

#195
Boston Psychic Studio
Area: Downtown
Address: 128 A Tremont St
Boston, MA 02108
Phone: (617) 956-0572

#196
Keiko Fine Japanese Handcraft
Area: Beacon Hill
Address: 121 Charles St
Boston, MA 02114
Phone: (617) 725-2888

#197
NK Gallery
Area: Chinatown
Address: 450 Harrison Ave
Boston, MA 02111
Phone: (603) 321-0632

#198
Katherine Houston Porcelain
Area: South Boston
Address: 81A Wareham St
Boston, MA 02118
Phone: (617) 695-6880

#199
A Brand Tickets
Area: Downtown
Address: 120212 Lafayette Ave
Boston, MA 02112
Phone: (617) 670-1800

#200
**North End Music and
Performing Arts Center**
Area: North End
Address: 16 Charter St
Boston, MA 02113
Phone: (617) 227-2270

#201
Coolidge Corner Theatre
Category: Cinema
Area: Coolidge Corner
Address: 290 Harvard St
Brookline, MA 02215
Phone: (617) 734-2500

#202
Styleboston
Area: South Boston
Address: 840 Summer St
Boston, MA 02127
Phone: (617) 765-0550

#203
Art Asylum Boston
Category: Art Gallery
Average price: Exclusive
Area: Mattapan
Address: 35 Sutton St
Boston, MA 02126
Phone: (617) 818-0724

#204
Boston Theatre Works
Area: Back Bay
Address: 31 Saint James Ave Ste 360
Boston, MA 02116
Phone: (617) 728-4321

#205
Boston Theatre Works
Category: Arts & Entertainment
Area: South End
Address: 325 Columbus Avenue Apt 11
Boston, MA 02116
Phone: (617) 939-9939

#206
Boston Dance Alliance
Area: South End
Address: 19 Clarendon St
Boston, MA 02116
Phone: (617) 456-6295

#207
**Commonwealth Shakespeare
Company Inc**
Area: South End
Address: 539 Tremont St
Boston, MA 02116
Phone: (617) 426-0863

#208
Berenberg Gallery
Area: South End
Address: 4 Clarendon Street
Boston, MA 02116
Phone: (617) 536-0800

#209
Little Virginia Winery
Area: Back Bay
Address: 44 Newbury
Boston, MA 02116
Phone: (617) 441-1858

#210
Plaster Fun Time Business
Area: Back Bay
Address: 45 Newbury St
Boston, MA 02116
Phone: (617) 262-1255

#211
Miller Block Gallery
Area: Back Bay
Address: 14 Newbury Street
Boston, MA 02116
Phone: (617) 536-4650

#212
Performing Arts
Physical Therapy, PC
Area: Back Bay
Address: 575 Boylston St
Boston, MA 02116
Phone: (617) 277-1500

#213
Galleria Florentia
Area: Back Bay
Address: 79 Newbury Street
Boston, MA 02116
Phone: (617) 585-9200

#214
Arden Gallery
Area: Back Bay
Address: 129 Newbury Street
Boston, MA 02116
Phone: (617) 247-0610

#215
Galerie Europeenne Inc
Area: Back Bay
Address: 129 Newbury St
Boston, MA 02116
Phone: (617) 859-7082

#216
Musica Vesuviana Italy Music Camp
Category: Summer Camp, Music Venues
Area: Back Bay
Address: 651 Boylston St
Boston, MA 02116
Phone: (339) 707-3593

#217
Rolly-Michaux Gallery
Area: Back Bay
Address: 290 Dartmouth
Boston, MA 02108
Phone: (617) 536-9898

#218
Victoria Munroe Fine Arts
Area: Back Bay
Address: 161 Newbury St Ste 1
Boston, MA 02116
Phone: (617) 523-0661

#219
Opera On Tap Boston
Category: Pub, Piano Bar
Area: Chinatown
Address: 37 Stuart St
Boston, MA 02116
Phone: (617) 338-8586

#220
Childs Gallery
Area: Back Bay
Address: 169 Newbury Street
Boston, MA 02116
Phone: (617) 266-1108

#221
Place Studio & Gallery
Category: Art Gallery
Area: South End
Address: 460 Harrison Ave
Boston, MA 02118
Phone: (877) 796-1076

#222
Walker Contemporary
Area: South End
Address: 450 Harrison Ave
Boston, MA 02118
Phone: (617) 695-0211

#223
Adelson Gallery
Area: South End
Address: 520 Harrison Ave
Boston, MA 02118
Phone: (617) 832-0633

#224
Victorian Society In America
Area: Back Bay
Address: 137 Beacon St
Boston, MA 02116
Phone: (617) 267-6338

#225
Keros Entertainment
Area: Back Bay
Address: 110 Beacon St
Boston, MA 02215
Phone: (617) 487-8807

#226
La Galería
Area: South End
Address: 85 W Newton St
Boston, MA 02118
Phone: (617) 927-1707

#227
China Arts Gallery
Area: Chinatown
Address: 72 Harrison Avenue
Boston, MA 02111
Phone: (617) 695-3731

#228
Copley Fine Art Auctions
Area: Back Bay
Address: 268 Newbury St
Boston, MA 02116
Phone: (617) 536-0030

#229
Jazz Bands
Area: South End
Address: 131 West Concord St.
Boston, MA 02118
Phone: (617) 312-3554

#230
Julie Chae Gallery
Area: South End
Address: 47 Thayer St
Boston, MA 02118
Phone: (617) 357-0001

#231
Bromfield Art Gallery
Area: South End
Address: 27 Thayer St
Boston, MA 02118
Phone: (617) 451-3605

#232
Psychic Readings
Area: Beacon Hill
Address: 109 Mount Vernon St
Boston, MA 02108
Phone: (617) 722-0098

#233
CNC Music Productions
Area: Back Bay
Address: 3 Boylston Place
Boston, MA 02116
Phone: (857) 445-7276

#234
Opera Boston
Area: Downtown
Address: 25 Kingston Street
Boston, MA 02111
Phone: (617) 451-3388

#235
JG & The MeggaTones
Area: Downtown
Address: 449 Washington St
Boston, MA 02111
Phone: (617) 799-9033

#236
Boston Hysterical Society
Area: Downtown
Address: 31 Milk St
Boston, MA 02109
Phone: (508) 872-7708

#237
Ayer Mansion
Area: Back Bay
Address: 395 Commonwealth Ave
Boston, MA 02215
Phone: (617) 536-2586

#238
The Bostonian Society
Area: Downtown
Address: 206 Washington St.
Boston, MA 02109
Phone: (617) 720-1713

#239
Bpo Consulting
Area: Financial District
Address: 60 State St
Boston, MA 02109
Phone: (617) 371-2980

#240
Mr Dooleys Irish Pub
Area: Financial District
Address: 77 Broad St
Boston, MA 02109
Phone: (617) 338-5656

#241
Boston Art
Area: Waterfront, South Boston
Address: 330 Congress St
Boston, MA 02210
Phone: (617) 951-0900

#242
I 8Ca
Area: Waterfront, South Boston
Address: 100 Northern Ave
Boston, MA 02210
Phone: (617) 478-3100

#243
Crosstown Arts
Area: North End
Address: 1 North Sq
Boston, MA 02113
Phone: (617) 720-0100

#244
Indigo Avenue
Area: Waterfront, South Boston
Address: 225 Northern Ave
Boston, MA 02210
Phone: (617) 314-2847

#245
PDB Music Tutoring
Area: Allston/Brighton
Address: 4 President Ter
Boston, MA 02134
Phone: (617) 784-2876

#246
**Maritime Museum
at Battery Wharf**
Area: North End
Address: Three Battery Wharf
Boston, MA 02109
Phone: (617) 994-9000

#247
Lamontagne Gallery
Area: South Boston
Address: 555 E 2nd St
Boston, MA 02127
Phone: (617) 464-4640

#248
Medicine Wheel Production
Area: South Boston
Address: 110 K St
Boston, MA 02127
Phone: (617) 268-6700

#249
The G Studio
Area: Dorchester
Address: 11 Humphreys St
Boston, MA 02125
Phone: (617) 265-0559

#250
Hull Lifesaving Museum
Area: South Boston
Address: 22 Drydock Ave
Boston, MA 02210
Phone: (617) 443-1900

#251
Chris MacRae - Voice Studio
Area: Allston/Brighton
Address: 855 Commonwealth Ave
Boston, MA 02215
Phone: (940) 600-0829

#252
Prolific Gamer Network
Area: Dorchester
Address: 68 Percival St Apt 2
Boston, MA 02122
Phone: (617) 905-2122

#253
East Boston Yacht Club
Category: Boating, Social Club
Area: East Boston
Address: 1 Rice St
Boston, MA 02128
Phone: (617) 567-9698

#254
Condor Street Studio
Category: Recording & Rehearsal Studio
Area: East Boston
Address: 100 Condor St
Boston, MA 02128
Phone: (617) 444-9532

#255
Eric Mauro
Area: Jamaica Plain
Address: 128 Brookside Ave
Boston, MA 02130
Phone: (857) 636-8445

#256
Mike Davidson Recording
Area: Allston/Brighton
Address: 52 Everett St
Boston, MA 02134
Phone: (800) 846-5495

#257
Edward M. Stanley
Appraisal Service
Area: Jamaica Plain
Address: 11 Bardwell St
Boston, MA 02130
Phone: (617) 983-5220

#258
Brattle Theatre
Category: Cinema
Area: Harvard Square
Address: 40 Brattle St
Cambridge, MA 02138
Phone: (617) 876-6837

#259
The Comedy Studio
Category: Comedy Club
Average price: Inexpensive
Area: Harvard Square
Address: 1238 Massachusetts Ave
Cambridge, MA 02138
Phone: (617) 661-6507

#260
Somerville Theatre
Category: Cinema
Area: Davis Square
Address: 55 Davis Sq
Somerville, MA 02144
Phone: (617) 625-5700

#261
Kendall Square Cinema
Category: Cinema
Area: Kendall Square/MIT
Address: 1 Kendall Sq
Cambridge, MA 02139
Phone: (617) 621-1202

#262
Voltage Coffee & Art
Category: Coffee & Tea, Art Gallery
Average price: Modest
Area: East Cambridge
Address: 295 3rd St
Cambridge, MA 02142
Phone: (617) 714-3974

#263
Harvard Film Archive
Category: Cinema
Area: Harvard Square
Address: 24 Quincy St
Cambridge, MA 02238
Phone: (617) 495-4700

#264
Club Passim
Category: Music Venues
Average price: Modest
Area: Harvard Square
Address: 47 Palmer St
Cambridge, MA 02138
Phone: (617) 492-7679

#265
Harvard Museum of Natural History
Category: Museum, Botanical Garden
Area: Harvard Square
Address: 26 Oxford St
Cambridge, MA 02138
Phone: (617) 495-3045

#266
Oberon
Category: Performing Arts, Bar
Average price: Modest
Area: Harvard Square
Address: 2 Arrow St
Cambridge, MA 02138
Phone: (617) 496-8004

#267
Lizard Lounge
Category: Music Venues, Burgers
Average price: Modest
Area: Porter Square
Address: 1667 Massachusetts Ave
Cambridge, MA 02138
Phone: (617) 547-0759

#268
Toad
Category: Music Venues,
Dance Club, Dive Bar
Average price: Inexpensive
Area: Porter Square
Address: 1912 Massachusetts Ave
Cambridge, MA 02140
Phone: (617) 497-4950

#269
MIT Museum
Category: Museum
Area: Kendall Square/MIT
Address: 265 Massachusetts Ave
Cambridge, MA 02139
Phone: (617) 253-5927

#270
Great Scott
Category: Dance Club,
Lounge, Music Venues
Average price: Inexpensive
Area: Allston/Brighton
Address: 1222 Commonwealth Ave
Allston, MA 02134
Phone: (617) 566-9014

#271
ImprovBoston Theatre
Category: Performing Arts,
Comedy Club, Venues, Event Space
Average price: Inexpensive
Area: Central Square
Address: 40 Prospect St
Cambridge, MA 02139
Phone: (617) 576-1253

#272
Museum of Bad Art
Category: Museum
Area: Davis Square
Address: 55 Davis Sq
Somerville, MA 02143
Phone: (781) 444-6757

#273
Cantab Lounge
Category: Lounge, Music Venues
Average price: Inexpensive
Area: Central Square
Address: 738 Massachusetts Ave
Cambridge, MA 02139
Phone: (617) 354-2685

#274
Capitol Theatre
Category: Cinema
Area: East Arlington
Address: 204 Massachusetts Ave
Arlington, MA 02474
Phone: (781) 648-4340

#275
Johnny D's
Category: Bar, Music Venues
Average price: Modest
Area: Davis Square
Address: 17 Holland St
Somerville, MA 02144
Phone: (617) 776-2004

#276
The Lily Pad
Category: Performing Arts,
Music Venues, Jazz & Blues
Average price: Inexpensive
Area: Inman Square
Address: 1353 Cambridge St
Cambridge, MA 02139
Phone: (617) 395-1393

#277
Midway Cafe
Category: Music Venues, Bar, Karaoke
Average price: Inexpensive
Area: Jamaica Plain
Address: 3496 Washington St
Jamaica Plain, MA 02130
Phone: (617) 524-9038

#278
Seyyide Belly Dance
Category: Performing Arts
Area: Harvard Square
Address: 400 Harvard St
Cambridge, MA 02140
Phone: (774) 473-9785

#279
Central Square Theater
Category: Performing Arts
Area: Central Square
Address: 450 Mass Ave
Cambridge, MA 02139
Phone: (866) 811-4111

#280
The Sinclair
Category: Music Venues
Average price: Modest
Area: Harvard Square
Address: 52 Church St
Cambridge, MA 02138
Phone: (617) 547-5200

#281
Zume's Coffee House
Category: Coffee & Tea, Art Gallery
Average price: Inexpensive
Area: Charlestown
Address: 221 Main St
Charlestown, MA 02129
Phone: (617) 242-0038

#282
Mr. Dooley's
Category: Bar, Irish, Music Venues
Average price: Modest
Area: Financial District
Address: 77 Broad St
Boston, MA 02109
Phone: (617) 338-5656

#283
Hamill Gallery of African Art
Category: Antiques, Art Gallery
Average price: Inexpensive
Area: Dudley Square
Address: 2164 Washington St
Roxbury, MA 02119
Phone: (617) 442-8204

#284
Footlight Club
Category: Performing Arts
Area: Jamaica Plain
Address: 7A Eliot St
Jamaica Plain, MA 02130
Phone: (617) 524-3200

#285
Harmonix Music Systems
Category: Arts & Entertainment
Area: Central Square
Address: 625 Massachusetts Ave
Cambridge, MA 02139
Phone: (617) 000-0000

#286
O'Briens Pub
Category: Pub, Music Venues
Average price: Inexpensive
Area: Allston/Brighton
Address: 3 Harvard Ave
Allston, MA 02134
Phone: (617) 782-6245

#287
Feet of Clay Pottery
Category: Art Gallery, Leisure Center
Average price: Modest
Area: Brookline Village
Address: 21 Station Street
Brookline, MA 02445
Phone: (617) 731-3262

#288
Multicultural Arts Center
Category: Venues, Art Gallery
Average price: Modest
Area: East Cambridge
Address: 41 2nd St
Cambridge, MA 02141
Phone: (617) 577-1400

#289
Puppet Showplace Theatre
Category: Performing Arts,
Party & Event Planning
Area: Brookline Village
Address: 32 Station St
Brookline, MA 02445
Phone: (617) 731-6400

#290
13Forest Gallery
Category: Art Gallery
Average price: Modest
Area: East Arlington
Address: 167A Massachusetts Ave
Arlington, MA 02474
Phone: (781) 641-3333

#291
The Hallway Gallery
Category: Art Gallery, Performing Arts
Average price: Modest
Area: Jamaica Plain
Address: 66A South St
Jamaica Plain, MA 02130
Phone: (617) 818-5996

#292
Café Gato Rojo
Category: Coffee & Tea, Art Gallery,
Music Venues
Average price: Inexpensive
Area: Harvard Square
Address: Harvard Yard
Cambridge, MA 02138
Phone: (617) 496-4658

#293
The Picture Place
Category: Framing, Art Gallery
Average price: Modest
Area: Coolidge Corner
Address: 320 Harvard St
Brookline, MA 02446
Phone: (617) 277-4357

#294
Cambridge Art & Frame
Category: Art Gallery, Framing
Average price: Modest
Area: East Cambridge
Address: 101 1st St
Cambridge, MA 02141
Phone: (617) 547-5944

#295
Paradise Rock Club
Category: Bar, Music Venues
Average price: Modest
Area: Allston/Brighton
Address: 967 Commonwealth Ave
Boston, MA 02215
Phone: (617) 562-8800

#296
East Meets West Bookstore
Category: Bookstore, Performing Arts,
Music Venues
Average price: Inexpensive
Area: Central Square
Address: 934 Massachusetts Ave
Cambridge, MA 02139
Phone: (617) 354-9596

#297
Charlestown Working Theater
Category: Performing Arts
Area: Charlestown
Address: 442 Bunker Hill Street
Charlestown, MA 02129
Phone: (617) 242-3285

#298
Masacote Entertainment
Category: Performing Arts,
Dance School
Area: East Cambridge
Address: 215 1st St
Cambridge, MA 02142
Phone: (617) 286-6272

#299
Cutler Majestic Theatre
Category: Performing Arts
Area: South End
Address: 219 Tremont St
Boston, MA 02116
Phone: (617) 824-8000

#300
Salsa Y Control
Category: Performing Arts,
Dance Studio, Dance School
Area: Allston/Brighton
Address: 161 Harvard Ave
Allston, MA 02138
Phone: (617) 312-6464

#301
**Tommy Doyles
Irish Pub & Restaurant**
Category: Irish, Pub, Music Venues
Average price: Modest
Area: Kendall Square/MIT
Address: 1 Kendall Sq
Cambridge, MA 02139
Phone: (617) 225-0888

#302
Battle of Bunker Hill Museum
Category: Tour, Museum
Area: Charlestown
Address: 43 Monument Sq
Charlestown, MA 02129
Phone: (617) 242-7275

#303
Aviary Gallery & Art Boutique
Category: Art Gallery
Average price: Modest
Area: Jamaica Plain
Address: 48 South St
Jamaica Plain, MA 02130
Phone: (617) 477-4728

#304
The Baak Gallery
Category: Jewelry, Art Gallery
Average price: Modest
Area: Harvard Square
Address: 35A Brattle St
Cambridge, MA 02138
Phone: (617) 354-0407

#305
Regattabar Jazz Club
Category: Jazz & Blues
Average price: Modest
Area: Harvard Square
Address: 1 Bennett St
Cambridge, MA 02138
Phone: (617) 661-5000

#306
Harvard Semitic Museum
Category: Museum
Area: Harvard Square
Address: 6 Divinity Ave
Cambridge, MA 02138
Phone: (617) 495-4631

#307
Heroes
Category: Music Venues, Dance Club
Average price: Modest
Area: Harvard Square
Address: 10 Brookline St
Cambridge, MA 02238
Phone: (617) 492-0082

#308
Art & Soul
Category: Yoga, Performing Arts
Area: Inman Square
Address: 91 Hampshire St
Cambridge, MA 02139
Phone: (617) 395-4227

#309
MIT List Visual Arts Center
Category: Art Gallery
Average price: Inexpensive
Area: Kendall Square/MIT
Address: 20 Ames St
Cambridge, MA 02139
Phone: (617) 253-4680

#310
The Slutcracker: A Burlesque
Category: Performing Arts
Area: Davis Square
Address: 55 Davis Sq
Somerville, MA 02144
Phone: (617) 625-5700

#311
The Distillery
Category: Arts & Entertainment
Area: South Boston
Address: 516 E Second St South
Boston, MA 02127
Phone: (617) 448-6691

#312
Byzantino
Category: Art Gallery
Average price: Modest
Area: East Cambridge
Address: 355 Cambridge St
Cambridge, MA 02141
Phone: (617) 868-0144

#313
USS Constitution
Category: Museum
Area: Charlestown
Address: 5th St 24
Charlestown, MA 02129
Phone: (617) 242-0543

#314
The Donkey Show
Category: Performing Arts, Dance Club
Average price: Modest
Area: Harvard Square
Address: 2 Arrow St Mid-
Cambridge, MA 02138
Phone: (617) 496-8004

#315
Fire Opal
Category: Jewelry, Women's Clothing,
Flowers, Gifts, Art Gallery, Arts, Crafts
Average price: Expensive
Area: Coolidge Corner
Address: 320 Harvard St
Brookline, MA 02445
Phone: (617) 739-9066

#316
Hasty Pudding Theatre
Category: Performing Arts
Area: Harvard Square
Address: 12 Holyoke St
Cambridge, MA 02138
Phone: (617) 496-8400

#317
**Peabody Museum
of Archaeology & Ethnology**
Category: Museum
Area: Harvard Square
Address: 11 Divinity Ave
Cambridge, MA 02138
Phone: (617) 496-1027

#318
Axiom
Category: Art Gallery, Museum
Area: Jamaica Plain
Address: 141 Green St
Jamaica Plain, MA 02130
Phone: (617) 676-5904

#319
29 Newbury Street Restaurant
Category: Art Gallery, Café
Average price: Expensive
Area: Back Bay
Address: 29 Newbury St
Boston, MA 02116
Phone: (617) 536-0290

#320
SuperShag Dance Studio
Category: Dance Studio,
Performing Arts, Dance School
Area: Charlestown
Address: 42 8th St
Charlestown, MA 02129
Phone: (781) 894-7424

#321
Regent Theatre
Category: Music Venues, Performing Arts
Average price: Inexpensive
Area: Arlington Center
Address: 7 Medford St
Arlington, MA 02474
Phone: (781) 646-4849

#322
Fresh Pond Ballet
Category: Dance School, Opera & Ballet
Area: Porter Square
Address: 1798 Massachusetts Ave
Cambridge, MA 02140
Phone: (617) 491-5865

#323
Out of the Blue Art Gallery
Category: Art Gallery
Average price: Modest
Area: Central Square
Address: 106 Prospect St
Cambridge, MA 02139
Phone: (617) 354-5287

#324
Brighton Music Hall
Category: Music Venues, Lounge
Average price: Modest
Area: Allston/Brighton
Address: 158 Brighton Avenue
Boston, MA 02134
Phone: (617) 779-0140

#325
Boston Red Sox
Category: Professional Sports Team
Area: Fenway
Address: 4 Yawkey Way
Boston, MA 02215
Phone: (617) 585-0300

#326
Strand Theatre
Category: Performing Arts
Area: Dorchester, Uphams Corner
Address: 543 Columbia Rd
Dorchester, MA 02125
Phone: (617) 635-1403

#327
From Russia with Art
Category: Art Gallery
Area: North Cambridge, Porter Square
Address: 1977 Massachusetts Ave
Cambridge, MA 02140
Phone: (617) 714-3055

#328
**Gateway ArtsCraft Store
& Art Gallery**
Category: Arts, Crafts, Art Gallery
Average price: Modest
Area: Brookline Village
Address: 60-62 Harvard St
Brookline, MA 02445
Phone: (617) 734-1577

#329
Jose Mateo Ballet Theatre
Category: Performing Arts
Area: Harvard Square
Address: 400 Harvard St
Cambridge, MA 02138
Phone: (617) 354-7467

#330
Pierre Menard Gallery
Category: Art Gallery
Area: Harvard Square
Address: 10 Arrow St
Cambridge, MA 02138
Phone: (617) 868-2033

#331
**Longy School of Music
of Bard College**
Category: Specialty School, Musical
Instruments & Teachers, Performing Arts
Average price: Inexpensive
Area: Harvard Square
Address: 27 Garden St
Cambridge, MA 02138
Phone: (617) 876-0956

#332
Jameson & Thompson Fine Art
Category: Art Gallery, Framing
Average price: Expensive
Area: Jamaica Plain
Address: 15 Greenview Ave
Jamaica Plain, MA 02130
Phone: (617) 524-1805

#333
UFORGE Gallery
Category: Art Gallery
Average price: Modest
Area: Jamaica Plain
Address: 767 Centre St
Jamaica Plain, MA 02130
Phone: (617) 553-4480

#334
DCR Hatch Memorial Shell
Category: Music Venues, Performing Arts
Average price: Inexpensive
Area: Beacon Hill
Address: 1 David G Mugar Way
Boston, MA 02114
Phone: (617) 263-1184

#335
Boston Chamber Music Society
Category: Performing Arts
Area: East Cambridge
Address: 60 Gore St
Cambridge, MA 02141
Phone: (617) 349-0086

#336
**Food Truck Festival
of New England**
Category: Festival
Area: Allston/Brighton
Address: 214 Lincoln St
Allston, MA 02134
Phone: (617) 782-7117

#337
Ace Ticket
Category: Performing Arts
Area: Allston/Brighton
Address: 1 Braintree St
Allston, MA 02134
Phone: (617) 783-3333

#338
Allston Village Main Streets
Category: Festival, Community
Service/Non-Profit
Area: Allston/Brighton
Address: 161 Harvard Ave
Allston, MA 02134
Phone: (617) 254-7564

#339
Dilboy Stadium
Category: Stadium/Arena
Area: East Arlington
Address: 110 Alewife Brook Pkwy
Somerville, MA 02144
Phone: (617) 628-0017

#340
Boston Casting
Category: Performing Arts
Area: Allston/Brighton
Address: 119 Braintree St
Allston, MA 02134
Phone: (617) 254-1001

#341
Boston Modern Orchestra Project
Category: Performing Arts
Area: Roslindale Village, Roslindale
Address: 9 Birch St
Roslindale, MA 02131
Phone: (617) 363-0396

#342
Susi's Gallery For Children
Category: Art Gallery
Average price: Expensive
Area: Huron Village
Address: 348 Huron Avenue
Cambridge, MA 02138
Phone: (617) 876-7874

#343
Davis Square Theatre
Category: Performing Arts
Area: Davis Square
Address: 255 Elm St
Somerville, MA 02144
Phone: (617) 684-5335

#344
Wild Goose Chase
Category: Women's Clothing,
Jewelry, Art Gallery
Average price: Modest
Area: Coolidge Corner
Address: 1355 Beacon St
Brookline, MA 02446
Phone: (617) 738-8020

#345
Wood & Strings Music Center
Category: Musical Instruments,
Music Venues
Average price: Exclusive
Area: Arlington Center
Address: 493 Massachusetts Ave
Arlington, MA 02474
Phone: (781) 641-2131

#346
Harvard Wine
Category: Winery, Beer, Wine, Spirits
Average price: Modest
Area: Porter Square
Address: 1664 Massachusetts Ave
Cambridge, MA 02138
Phone: (617) 547-3900

#347
Mass Motion Dance
Category: Performing Arts,
Dance Studio
Area: Allston/Brighton
Address: 100 Holton St
Brighton, MA 02135
Phone: (617) 562-0550

#348
Moves & Vibes Dance
Category: Performing Arts, Dance Studio
Area: East Cambridge
Address: 44 Fifth St
Cambridge, MA 02141
Phone: (617) 821-5884

#349
Cambridge Performing Arts Center
Category: Performing Arts, Yoga
Area: East Cambridge
Address: 535 Cambridge St
Cambridge, MA 02141
Phone: (617) 868-1118

#350
Belly Dance by Johara & Snake Dance Theater Company
Category: Performing Arts, Dance Studio
Area: Central Square
Address: 536 Mass Ave
Cambridge, MA 02139
Phone: (617) 780-8890

#351
Mobius Art Space
Category: Art Gallery,
Performing Arts, Music Venues
Average price: Inexpensive
Area: Central Square
Address: 55 Norfolk St
Cambridge, MA 02139
Phone: (617) 945-9481

#352
80 Border Street Cultural Exchange Center
Category: Performing Arts
Area: East Boston
Address: 80 Border St East
Boston, MA 02128
Phone: (617) 418-5060

#353
Cambridge Community Chorus
Category: Arts & Entertainment
Area: Central Square
Address: PO Box 390278
Cambridge, MA 02139
Phone: (617) 517-3169

#354
World Music/CRASHarts
Category: Performing Arts
Area: Central Square
Address: 720 Massachusetts Avenue
Cambridge, MA 02139
Phone: (617) 876-4275

#355
Zumix
Category: Music Venues,
Educational Service
Average price: Inexpensive
Area: East Boston
Address: 260 Sumner St East
Boston, MA 02128
Phone: (617) 568-9777

#356
Atlantic Works Gallery
Category: Art Gallery
Area: East Boston
Address: 80 Border St East
Boston, MA 02128
Phone: (978) 621-0737

#357
Beyond the 4th Wall
Category: Performing Arts
Area: Central Square
Address: 934 Massachusetts Ave
Cambridge, MA 02139
Phone: (617) 868-9900

#358
Brookline Historical Society Edward Devotion House
Category: Museum
Area: Coolidge Corner
Address: 347 Harvard Street
Brookline, MA 02446
Phone: (617) 566-5747

#359
MayFair in Harvard Square
Category: Festival
Area: Harvard Square
Address: 18 Brattle St
Cambridge, MA 02138
Phone: (617) 491-3434

#360
Fly Club
Category: Social Club
Area: Harvard Square
Address: 2 Holyoke Place
Cambridge, MA 02138
Phone: (617) 491-8191

#361
Independent Designers Market Boston
Category: Jewelry, Flowers,
Gifts, Art Gallery
Area: Harvard Square
Address: 30 Brattle St
Mid-Cambridge, MA 02138
Phone: (908) 420-1509

#362
Cambridge Forum
Category: Education
Area: Harvard Square
Address: 3 Church St
Cambridge, MA 02138
Phone: (617) 495-2727

#363
University Place Gallery
Category: Art Gallery
Area: Harvard Square
Address: 124 Mount Auburn St.
Cambridge, MA 02138
Phone: (617) 876-0246

#364
Cambridge Carnival International
Category: Festival,
Event Planning, Service
Area: Harvard Square
Address: 144 Mount Auburn St
Cambridge, MA 02138
Phone: (617) 863-0476

#365
Cambridge Hidden Kitchen
Category: Restaurant, Social Club
Average price: Expensive
Area: Huron Village
Address: Huron Village
Cambridge, MA
Phone: (617) 858-0179

#366
Ashmont Hill Chamber Music
Category: Performing Arts
Area: Dorchester
Address: 67 Ocean St
Dorchester, MA 02124
Phone: (617) 680-7542

#367
Ryles
Category: Jazz & Blues, Music Venues
Average price: Modest
Area: Inman Square
Address: 212 Hampshire St
Cambridge, MA 02139
Phone: (617) 876-9330

#368
DrumConnection
Category: Performing Arts, Musical
Instruments & Teachers
Average price: Modest
Area: East Arlington
Address: 177 Massachusetts Ave
Arlington, MA 02474
Phone: (781) 316-8068

#369
Cyrus Dallin Art Museum
Category: Museum
Area: Arlington Center
Address: 611 Massachusetts Ave
Arlington, MA 02474
Phone: (781) 641-0747

#370
Green Street Studio
Category: Performing Arts,
Dance School, Dance Studio
Area: Central Square
Address: 185 Green St
Cambridge, MA 02139
Phone: (617) 864-3191

#371
Simoni Rink
Category: Skating Rinks,
Stadium/Arena
Area: East Cambridge
Address: 155 Gore St
Cambridge, MA 02141
Phone: (617) 354-9523

#372
Harriet Tubman House
Category: Art Gallery
Area: South End
Address: 566 Columbus Avenue
Roxbury, MA 02118
Phone: (617) 536-8610

#373
Boston City Lights
Category: Performing Arts
Area: South Boston
Address: 1154 Washington St
Roxbury, MA 02118
Phone: (617) 695-2856

#374
Berwick Research Institute
Category: Art Gallery
Area: Dudley Square
Address: 14 Palmer St
Roxbury, MA 02119
Phone: (617) 442-4200

#375
CBC Great Pumpkin Fest
Category: Festival
Area: Kendall Square/MIT
Address: 1 Kendall Sq
Cambridge, MA 02139
Phone: (617) 494-1994

#376
New England Tango Academy
Category: Performing Arts, Dance School
Area: East Cambridge
Address: 620 Cambridge St.
Cambridge, MA 02141
Phone: (617) 229-5018

#377
Scullers Jazz Club
Category: Jazz & Blues, American
Average price: Modest
Area: Allston/Brighton
Address: 400 Soldiers Rd
Boston, MA 02134
Phone: (617) 562-4111

#378
Massasoit Lodge of Elks
Category: Social Club
Area: Central Square
Address: 55 Bishop Richard Allen Dr
Cambridge, MA 02139
Phone: (617) 354-0404

#379
Rumba Y Timbal Dance Company
Category: Performing Arts, Dance School
Area: Central Square
Address: 7 Temple St
Cambridge, MA 02139
Phone: (617) 543-7912

#380
Cambridge YMCA Theatre
Category: Performing Arts
Area: Central Square
Address: 820 Massachusetts Ave
Cambridge, MA 02238
Phone: (617) 661-9622

#381
Artist Group of Charlestown Arteria
Category: Art Gallery
Average price: Inexpensive
Area: Charlestown
Address: 523 Medford Street
Charlestown, MA 02129
Phone: (617) 241-0130

#382
Brighton-Allston Heritage Museum
Category: Museum, Art Gallery
Area: Allston/Brighton
Address: 20 Chestnut Hill Ave
Brighton Center, MA 02135
Phone: (617) 635-1436

#383
Notlob Parlor Concerts
Category: Music Venues, Performing Arts
Average price: Inexpensive
Area: Jamaica Plain
Address: 12 South St
Jamaica Plain, MA 02130
Phone: (413) 658-4585

#384
JP Art Market
Category: Art Gallery
Area: Jamaica Plain
Address: 36 South St
Jamaica Plain, MA 02130
Phone: (617) 522-1729

#385
ComedySportz Boston
Category: Performing Arts
Area: Davis Square
Address: 255 Elm Street
Somerville, MA 02144
Phone: (617) 426-1999

#386
The Artful Heart Gallery
Category: Arts, Crafts, Art Gallery
Average price: Modest
Area: Arlington Center
Address: 311 Broadway
Arlington, MA 02474
Phone: (781) 777-1533

#387
Porter Square Psychic Studio
Category: Psychic, Astrologer
Area: North Cambridge
Address: 1923 Mass Ave
Cambridge, MA 02140
Phone: (617) 492-0069

#388
Villa Victoria Center for the Arts
Category: Venues, Event Space,
Performing Arts, Cultural Center
Area: South End
Address: 85 W Newton St
Boston, MA 02118
Phone: (617) 927-1735

#389
Tall Tree Guild
Category: Home Decor, Art Gallery
Area: East Arlington
Address: 185 Massachusetts Ave
Arlington, MA 02474
Phone: (781) 646-3009

#390
About Hair
Category: Antiques, Art Gallery
Area: Harvard Square
Address: 1 Arrow St
Cambridge, MA 02138
Phone: (617) 868-8213

#391
Scullers Grille and Lounge
Category: Jazz & Blues
Area: Allston/Brighton
Address: 400 Soldiers Field Rd
Allston, MA 02134
Phone: (617) 783-0090

#392
Mobilia
Category: Art Gallery
Area: Huron Village
Address: 358 Huron Avenue
Cambridge, MA 02138
Phone: (617) 876-2109

#393
Kay's Oasis Function Hall
Category: Social Club
Area: Mattapan
Address: 1125 Blue Hill Ave
Dorchester Center, MA 02124
Phone: (617) 436-9566

#394
American Repertory Theater
Category: Performing Arts,
Colleges & Universities
Area: Harvard Square
Address: 64 Brattle St
Cambridge, MA 02138
Phone: (617) 547-8300

#395
Karina Mattei Jeweler Designer
Category: Jewelry, Art Gallery
Average price: Modest
Area: Coolidge Corner
Address: 318 Harvard St
Brookline, MA 02446
Phone: (617) 713-4450

#396
**Bay State Model
Railroad Museum**
Category: Museum
Area: Roslindale Village, Roslindale
Address: 760 South St
Roslindale, MA 02131
Phone: (617) 327-4341

#397
Red Fez
Category: Middle Eastern, Music Venues
Average price: Modest
Area: South End
Address: 1222 Washington St
Boston, MA 02118
Phone: (617) 338-6060

#398
The Dance Complex
Category: Performing Arts, Dance School
Area: Central Square
Address: 536 Massachusetts Ave
Cambridge, MA 02139
Phone: (617) 547-9363

#399
Harvard Collections Museum Store
Category: Museum
Area: Harvard Square
Address: 1350 Massachusetts Avenue
Cambridge, MA 02138
Phone: (617) 496-0700

#400
AMC Assembly Row 12
Category: Cinema
Area: Somerville
Address: 395 Artisan Way
Somerville, MA 02145

TOP 500 NIGHTLIFE

Most Recommended by Locals & Trevelers
Ranking (from #1 to #500)

#1
Improv Asylum
Category: Comedy Club
Average price: Modest
Area: North End
Address: 216 Hanover St
Boston, MA 02113
Phone: (617) 263-6887

#2
Drink
Category: Lounge, American
Average price: Expensive
Area: Waterfront, South Boston
Address: 348 Congress St
Boston, MA 02228
Phone: (617) 695-1806

#3
Wally's Cafe
Category: Jazz & Blues, Music Venues
Average price: Inexpensive
Area: South End
Address: 427 Massachusetts Ave
Boston, MA 02118
Phone: (617) 424-1408

#4
Biddy Early's
Category: Dive Bar
Average price: Inexpensive
Area: Financial District
Address: 141 Pearl St
Boston, MA 02110
Phone: (617) 654-9944

#5
The Hawthorne
Category: American, Cocktail Bar
Average price: Expensive
Area: Allston/Brighton
Address: 500A Commonwealth Ave
Boston, MA 02215
Phone: (617) 532-9150

#6
Croke Park/Whitey's
Category: Dive Bar
Average price: Inexpensive
Area: South Boston
Address: 268 W Broadway
Boston, MA 02127
Phone: (617) 464-4869

#7
Corner Tavern
Category: Bar, American
Average price: Modest
Area: Back Bay
Address: 421 Marlborough St
Boston, MA 02115
Phone: (617) 262-5555

#8
Franklin Café
Category: Lounge, American
Average price: Modest
Area: South End
Address: 278 Shawmut Ave
Boston, MA 02118
Phone: (617) 350-0010

#9
Cafe Gigu
Category: Café, Wine Bar
Average price: Modest
Area: East Boston
Address: 102 Meridian St
Boston, MA 02128
Phone: (617) 561-4448

#10
Jm Curley
Category: American, Lounge
Average price: Modest
Area: Downtown
Address: 21 Temple Pl
Boston, MA 02111
Phone: (617) 338-5333

#11
Bukowski Tavern
Category: Pub, American
Average price: Modest
Area: Back Bay
Address: 50 Dalton St
Boston, MA 02115
Phone: (617) 437-9999

#12
Paradise Rock Club
Category: Bar, Music Venues
Average price: Modest
Area: Allston/Brighton
Address: 967 Commonwealth Ave
Boston, MA 02215
Phone: (617) 562-8800

#13
The Lower Depths
Category: Pub
Average price: Modest
Area: Allston/Brighton
Address: 476 Commonwealth Ave
Boston, MA 02115
Phone: (617) 266-6662

#14
21st Amendment
Category: Bar
Average price: Modest
Area: Downtown, Beacon Hill
Address: 150 Bowdoin Sq
Boston, MA 02108
Phone: (617) 227-7100

#15
The Beehive
Category: Jazz & Blues, American,
Breakfast & Brunch
Average price: Expensive
Area: South End
Address: 541 Tremont St
Boston, MA 02116
Phone: (617) 423-0069

#16
Franklin Southie
Category: American, Lounge
Average price: Modest
Area: South Boston
Address: 152 Dorchester Ave
Boston, MA 02127
Phone: (617) 269-1003

#17
J J Foley's Cafe
Category: Pub, American
Average price: Modest
Area: South End
Address: 117 E Berkeley St
Boston, MA 02118
Phone: (617) 728-9101

#18
City Bar
Category: Lounge, American
Average price: Expensive
Area: Back Bay
Address: 61 Exeter St
Boston, MA 02199
Phone: (617) 536-5300

#19
Darryl's Corner Bar & Kitchen
Category: Bar, Jazz & Blues
Average price: Modest
Area: South End
Address: 604 Columbus Ave
Boston, MA 02118
Phone: (617) 536-1100

#20
Woody's Grill and Tap
Category: Bar, American, Pizza
Average price: Modest
Area: Allston/Brighton
Address: 58 Hemenway St
Boston, MA 02115
Phone: (617) 375-9663

#21
Lucky's Lounge
Category: Lounge, American
Average price: Modest
Area: Waterfront, South Boston
Address: 355 Congress St
Boston, MA 02210
Phone: (617) 357-5825

#22
Scullers Jazz Club
Category: Jazz & Blues, American
Average price: Modest
Area: Allston/Brighton
Address: 400 Soldiers Rd
Boston, MA 02134
Phone: (617) 562-4111

#23
Intermission Tavern
Category: Bar, American, Burgers
Average price: Modest
Area: Back Bay
Address: 228 Tremont St
Boston, MA 02116
Phone: (617) 451-5997

#24
Corner Cafe
Category: Dive Bar, American
Average price: Inexpensive
Area: North End
Address: 87 Prince St
Boston, MA 02113
Phone: (617) 523-8997

#25
Lolita Cocina & Tequila Bar
Category: Mexican, Lounge, Cocktail Bar
Average price: Expensive
Area: Back Bay
Address: 271 Dartmouth St
Boston, MA 02116
Phone: (617) 369-5609

#26
The Pour House
Category: Bar, American
Average price: Inexpensive
Area: Back Bay
Address: 907 Boylston St
Boston, MA 02115
Phone: (617) 236-1767

#27
Stoddard's Fine Food & Ale
Category: Bar, American, Gastropub
Average price: Modest
Area: Downtown
Address: 48 Temple Pl
Boston, MA 02111
Phone: (617) 426-0048

#28
The Corner Pub
Category: Dive Bar, Pub
Average price: Inexpensive
Area: Waterfront, Leather District
Address: 162 Lincoln St
Boston, MA 02111
Phone: (617) 542-7080

#29
Tip Tap Room
Category: American, Bar, Gastropub
Average price: Modest
Area: Beacon Hill
Address: 138 Cambridge St
Boston, MA 02114
Phone: (857) 350-3344

#30
Local 149
Category: Pub, American
Average price: Modest
Area: South Boston
Address: 149 P St
Boston, MA 02127
Phone: (617) 269-0900

#31
Battery Park Bar & Lounge
Category: American, Lounge, Sports Bar
Average price: Modest
Area: Financial District
Address: 33 Batterymarch St
Boston, MA 02110
Phone: (617) 350-7275

#32
Sister Sorel
Category: Bar, American
Average price: Modest
Area: South End
Address: 645 Tremont St
Boston, MA 02116
Phone: (617) 266-4600

#33
Ward 8
Category: Cocktail Bar, American
Average price: Modest
Area: North End
Address: 90 N Washington St
Boston, MA 02113
Phone: (617) 823-4478

#34
The Bar at Taj Boston
Category: Bar
Average price: Expensive
Area: Back Bay
Address: 15 Arlington St
Boston, MA 02116
Phone: (617) 536-5700

#35
Post 390
Category: Bar, American
Average price: Expensive
Area: Back Bay
Address: 406 Stuart St
Boston, MA 02116
Phone: (617) 399-0015

#36
The Lansdowne Pub
Category: Pub
Average price: Modest
Area: Fenway
Address: 9 Lansdowne St
Boston, MA 02215
Phone: (617) 247-1222

#37
OTTO
Category: Pizza, Bar
Average price: Modest
Area: Allston/Brighton
Address: 888 Commonwealth Ave
Boston, MA 02215
Phone: (617) 232-0447

#38
Last Hurrah
Category: Bar, American
Average price: Modest
Area: Downtown
Address: 60 School St
Boston, MA 02108
Phone: (617) 227-8600

#39
Tavern Road
Category: American, Bar
Average price: Expensive
Area: Waterfront, South Boston
Address: 343 Congress St
Boston, MA 02210
Phone: (617) 790-0808

#40
The Junction
Category: Bar, American
Average price: Modest
Area: South Boston
Address: 110 Dorchester St
Boston, MA 02127
Phone: (617) 268-6429

#41
Granary Tavern
Category: American, Pub
Average price: Modest
Area: Financial District
Address: 170 Milk St
Boston, MA 02109
Phone: (617) 449-7110

#42
Black Horse Tavern
Category: Dive Bar
Average price: Inexpensive
Area: North End
Address: 340 Faneuil Hall Mrkt Pl
Boston, MA 02109
Phone: (617) 227-2038

#43
Crossroads Irish Pub
Category: Pub, Irish
Average price: Inexpensive
Area: Back Bay
Address: 495 Beacon St
Boston, MA 02115
Phone: (857) 233-5943

#44
Church
Category: American, Music Venues
Average price: Modest
Area: Fenway
Address: 69 Kilmarnock St
Boston, MA 02215
Phone: (617) 236-7600

#45
JJ Foley's
Category: Pub
Average price: Inexpensive
Area: Downtown
Address: 21 Kingston St
Boston, MA 02111
Phone: (617) 695-2529

#46
The Sevens Ale House
Category: Pub, American
Average price: Modest
Area: Beacon Hill
Address: 77 Charles St
Boston, MA 02114
Phone: (617) 523-9074

#47
Amrheins
Category: American, Bar
Average price: Modest
Area: South Boston
Address: 80 W Broadway
Boston, MA 02127
Phone: (617) 268-6189

#48
Jacob Wirth Restaurant
Category: German, Pub
Average price: Modest
Area: Chinatown
Address: 31-37 Stuart St
Boston, MA 02116
Phone: (617) 356-8390

#49
Beacon Hill Pub
Category: Pub
Average price: Inexpensive
Area: Beacon Hill
Address: 149 Charles St
Boston, MA 02108
Phone: (617) 625-7100

#50
The Littlest Bar
Category: Pub
Average price: Modest
Area: Financial District
Address: 102 Broad St
Boston, MA 02110
Phone: (617) 542-8469

#51
Harvard Garden
Category: Bar, American
Average price: Modest
Area: Beacon Hill
Address: 316 Cambridge St
Boston, MA 02114
Phone: (617) 523-2727

#52
Tom English's Cottage
Category: Bar
Average price: Inexpensive
Area: South Boston
Address: 118 Emerson St
Boston, MA 02127
Phone: (617) 269-9805

#53
Sunset Cantina
Category: Mexican, Bar
Average price: Modest
Area: Allston/Brighton
Address: 916 Commonwealth Ave
Boston, MA 02215
Phone: (617) 731-8646

#54
Pellino's Ristorante
Category: Bar, Italian
Average price: Modest
Area: North End
Address: 2 Prince St
Boston, MA 02109
Phone: (617) 227-7300

#55
Solas
Category: Pub, Irish
Average price: Modest
Area: Back Bay
Address: 710 Boylston St
Boston, MA 02199
Phone: (617) 933-4803

#56
Bostonia Public House
Category: Lounge, American
Average price: Expensive
Area: Financial District
Address: 131 State St
Boston, MA 02109
Phone: (617) 948-9800

#57
Kelley Square Pub
Category: Pub, American, Mexican
Average price: Modest
Area: East Boston
Address: 84 Bennington St
Boston, MA 02128
Phone: (617) 567-4627

#58
Prima e Dopo
Category: Bar
Average price: Modest
Area: East Boston
Address: 300 Saratoga St
Boston, MA 02128
Phone: (617) 874-8156

#59
The Gas @ Great Scott
Category: Comedy Club
Average price: Inexpensive
Area: Allston/Brighton
Address: 1222 Commonwealth Ave
Boston, MA 02134
Phone: (617) 566-9014

#60
Bar 10
Category: Lounge, American
Average price: Modest
Area: Back Bay
Address: 10 Huntington Ave
Boston, MA 02116
Phone: (617) 424-7446

#61
Avery Bar
Category: Bar
Average price: Expensive
Area: Chinatown
Address: 10 Avery St
Boston, MA 02111
Phone: (617) 574-7100

#62
Minibar Boston
Category: Lounge
Average price: Expensive
Area: Back Bay
Address: 51 Huntington Ave
Boston, MA 02116
Phone: (617) 424-8500

#63
The Brahmin
Category: American, Lounge
Average price: Modest
Area: Back Bay
Address: 33 Stanhope St
Boston, MA 02116
Phone: (617) 723-3131

#64
The Kinsale
Category: Pub, Irish, Karaoke
Average price: Modest
Area: Downtown
Address: 2 Center Plz
Boston, MA 02108
Phone: (617) 742-5577

#65
Eugene O'Neill's
Category: Pub
Average price: Modest
Area: Jamaica Plain
Address: 3700 Washington St
Boston, MA 02130
Phone: (617) 553-2492

#66
Highball Lounge
Category: Lounge, Cocktail Bar
Average price: Modest
Area: Downtown
Address: 90 Tremont St
Boston, MA 02108
Phone: (617) 772-0202

#67
Les Zygomates
Category: French, Jazz & Blues, Venues, Event Space
Average price: Expensive
Area: Waterfront, Leather District
Address: 129 South St
Boston, MA 02111
Phone: (617) 542-5108

#68
6B Lounge
Category: Lounge
Average price: Modest
Area: Downtown
Address: 6 Beacon St
Boston, MA 02108
Phone: (617) 742-0306

#69
Nix's Mate
Category: Lounge
Average price: Modest
Area: Financial District
Address: 89 Broad St
Boston, MA 02110
Phone: (617) 348-1234

#70
Shenannigan's Irish Pub & Restaurant
Category: Bar, American
Average price: Modest
Area: South Boston
Address: 332 W Broadway
Boston, MA 02127
Phone: (617) 269-9509

#71
RISE
Category: Dance Club
Average price: Modest
Area: Back Bay
Address: 306 Stuart St
Boston, MA 02116
Phone: (617) 423-7473

#72
Red Fez
Category: Middle Eastern, Music Venues
Average price: Modest
Area: South End
Address: 1222 Washington St
Boston, MA 02118
Phone: (617) 338-6060

#73
The Red Room @ Cafe 939
Category: Coffee & Tea, Music Venues
Average price: Inexpensive
Area: Back Bay
Address: 939 Boylston St
Boston, MA 02115
Phone: (617) 747-2261

#74
Brighton Music Hall
Category: Music Venues, Lounge
Average price: Modest
Area: Allston/Brighton
Address: 158 Brighton Avenue
Boston, MA 02134
Phone: (617) 779-0140

#75
Stats Bar & Grille
Category: Sports Bar, American
Average price: Modest
Area: South Boston
Address: 77 Dorchester St
Boston, MA 02127
Phone: (617) 268-9300

#76
L Street Tavern
Category: Bar
Average price: Inexpensive
Area: South Boston
Address: 658A E 8th St
Boston, MA 02127
Phone: (617) 268-4335

#77
Cactus Club Restaurant & Bar
Category: Mexican, Bar
Average price: Modest
Area: Back Bay
Address: 939 Boylston St
Boston, MA 02115
Phone: (617) 236-0200

#78
Cask'n Flagon
Category: Sports Bar, American
Average price: Modest
Area: Fenway
Address: 62 Brookline Ave
Boston, MA 02215
Phone: (617) 536-4840

#79
The Landing
Category: Bar
Average price: Modest
Area: Waterfront
Address: One Long Wharf
Boston, MA 02110
Phone: (617) 227-4321

#80
The Hill Tavern
Category: Pub, Breakfast & Brunch
Average price: Modest
Area: Beacon Hill
Address: 228 Cambridge St
Boston, MA 02114
Phone: (617) 742-6192

#81
The Boston Sail Loft
Category: Bar, American
Average price: Modest
Area: North End
Address: 80 Atlantic Ave
Boston, MA 02110
Phone: (617) 227-7280

#82
Bleacher Bar
Category: Sports Bar
Average price: Modest
Area: Fenway
Address: 82 Lansdowne St
Boston, MA 02228
Phone: (617) 262-2424

#83
M Bar & Lounge
Category: Lounge
Average price: Expensive
Area: Back Bay
Address: 776 Boylston St
Boston, MA 02199
Phone: (617) 535-8800

#84
Beantown Pub
Category: Pub, American
Average price: Modest
Area: Downtown
Address: 100 Tremont St
Boston, MA 02108
Phone: (617) 426-0111

#85
Baseball Tavern
Category: Sports Bar
Average price: Inexpensive
Area: Fenway
Address: 1270 Boylston St
Boston, MA 02215
Phone: (617) 867-6526

#86
Bond Restaurant | Lounge
Category: Lounge
Average price: Expensive
Area: Financial District
Address: 250 Franklin St
Boston, MA 02110
Phone: (617) 956-8756

#87
McGreevy's
Category: Sports Bar, Irish
Average price: Modest
Area: Back Bay
Address: 911 Boylston St
Boston, MA 02115
Phone: (617) 262-0911

#88
OAK Long Bar
Category: Bar, American
Average price: Expensive
Area: Back Bay
Address: 138 St James Ave
Boston, MA 02116
Phone: (617) 585-7222

#89
**Scholars American
Bistro & Cocktail Lounge**
Category: American, Lounge, Pool Hall
Average price: Modest
Area: Downtown
Address: 25 School St
Boston, MA 02108
Phone: (617) 248-0025

#90
Eddie C's Bar
Category: Dive Bar
Average price: Inexpensive
Area: East Boston
Address: 34 Maverick Sq
Boston, MA 02128
Phone: (617) 567-9395

#91
Storyville
Category: Lounge, Dance Club
Average price: Modest
Area: Back Bay
Address: 90 Exeter St
Boston, MA 02116
Phone: (617) 236-1134

#92
Vino Volo
Category: Wine Bar
Average price: Modest
Area: East Boston
Address: 1 Harborside Dr
Boston, MA 02128
Phone: (617) 568-0051

#93
Red Hat
Category: Dive Bar, American
Average price: Modest
Area: Downtown, Beacon Hill
Address: 9 Bowdoin St
Boston, MA 02114
Phone: (617) 523-2175

#94
Aragosta
Category: Italian, Bar
Average price: Expensive
Area: North End
Address: 3 Battery Wharf
Boston, MA 02109
Phone: (617) 994-9001

#95
The Living Room
Category: Lounge, Breakfast & Brunch
Average price: Modest
Area: Waterfront, North End
Address: 101 Atlantic Ave
Boston, MA 02110
Phone: (617) 723-5101

#96
Waterfront Cafe
Category: Café, Sports Bar
Average price: Modest
Area: North End
Address: 450 Commercial St
Boston, MA 02109
Phone: (617) 523-4055

#97
**Howl At The Moon
Dueling Piano Bar**
Category: Bar, Music Venues
Average price: Modest
Area: Financial District
Address: 184 High St
Boston, MA 02110
Phone: (617) 292-4695

#98
The Vault
Category: American, Bar
Average price: Modest
Area: Financial District
Address: 105 Water St
Boston, MA 02109
Phone: (617) 292-3355

#99
Wink & Nod
Category: Cocktail Bar, American
Average price: Expensive
Area: South End
Address: 3 Appleton St
Boston, MA 02116
Phone: (617) 482-0117

#100
Brownstone
Category: Bar, Salad
Average price: Modest
Area: Back Bay
Address: 111 Dartmouth St
Boston, MA 02116
Phone: (617) 867-4142

#101
Empire
Category: Lounge, Asian Fusion
Average price: Expensive
Area: Waterfront, South Boston
Address: 1 Marina Park Dr
Boston, MA 02210
Phone: (617) 295-0001

#102
RumBa
Category: Lounge
Average price: Expensive
Area: Waterfront, South Boston
Address: 510 Atlantic Ave
Boston, MA 02210
Phone: (617) 217-5148

#103
Champion's Boston
Sports Bar & Restaurant
Category: Sports Bar, American
Average price: Modest
Area: Back Bay
Address: 110 Huntington Ave
Boston, MA 02116
Phone: (617) 927-5304

#104
BoMA
Category: Bar, American
Average price: Modest
Area: South End
Address: 1415 Washington St
Boston, MA 02118
Phone: (617) 536-2662

#105
Vintage Lounge
Category: Lounge, American
Average price: Expensive
Area: Financial District
Address: 72 Broad St
Boston, MA 02110
Phone: (617) 482-1900

#106
M.J. O'Connor's Irish Pub
Category: Pub, American
Average price: Modest
Area: Back Bay
Address: 27 Columbus Ave
Boston, MA 02116
Phone: (617) 482-2255

#107
Murphy's Law
Category: Restaurant, Pub
Average price: Inexpensive
Area: South Boston
Address: 837 Summer St
Boston, MA 02127
Phone: (617) 269-6667

#108
Mr. Dooley's
Category: Bar, Irish, Music Venues
Average price: Modest
Area: Financial District
Address: 77 Broad St
Boston, MA 02109
Phone: (617) 338-5656

#109
The Playwright
Category: American, Sports Bar
Average price: Modest
Area: South Boston
Address: 658 E Broadway
Boston, MA 02127
Phone: (617) 269-2537

#110
Jillian's & Lucky Strike
Category: Pool Hall, Bowling
Average price: Modest
Area: Fenway
Address: 145 Ipswich St
Boston, MA 02115
Phone: (617) 437-0300

#111
The Barracuda Tavern
Category: Bar, Seafood, American
Average price: Modest
Area: Downtown
Address: 15 Bosworth St
Boston, MA 02108
Phone: (617) 482-0301

#112
Hub Pub
Category: Restaurant, Pub
Average price: Inexpensive
Area: Downtown
Address: 18 Province St
Boston, MA 02108
Phone: (617) 227-8952

#113
Barney Fanning's
Category: Irish, Pub, Irish Pub
Average price: Modest
Area: Financial District
Address: 99 Broad St
Boston, MA 02110
Phone: (617) 357-8287

#114
Dillon's
Category: Bar, American
Average price: Modest
Area: Back Bay
Address: 955 Boylston St
Boston, MA 02115
Phone: (617) 421-1818

#115
House Of Blues Boston
Category: Venues, Event Space,
Jazz & Blues
Average price: Modest
Area: Fenway
Address: 15 Lansdowne St
Boston, MA 02215
Phone: (800) 653-8000

#116
Clerys Bar & Restaurant
Category: Bar, American
Average price: Modest
Area: Back Bay
Address: 113 Dartmouth St
Boston, MA 02116
Phone: (617) 262-9874

#117
Cheers
Category: Bar, Restaurant
Average price: Modest
Area: Beacon Hill
Address: 84 Beacon St
Boston, MA 02108
Phone: (617) 227-9605

#118
Jerry Remy's Sports Bar & Grill
Category: Sports Bar, American
Average price: Modest
Area: Fenway
Address: 1265 Boylston St
Boston, MA 02215
Phone: (617) 236-7369

#119
Bill's Bar & Lounge
Category: Sports Bar, Music Venues
Average price: Modest
Area: Fenway
Address: 5 Lansdowne St
Boston, MA 02215
Phone: (617) 247-1222

#120
Emmet's Irish Pub & Restaurant
Category: Pub, Irish, Burgers
Average price: Modest
Area: Downtown
Address: 6B Beacon St
Boston, MA 02108
Phone: (617) 742-8565

#121
Umbria Prime
Category: Lounge, Steakhouse
Average price: Expensive
Area: Financial District
Address: 295 Franklin St
Boston, MA 02228
Phone: (617) 338-1000

#122
Underbar
Category: Dance Club,
Party & Event Planning
Average price: Expensive
Area: Back Bay
Address: 279 Tremont St
Boston, MA 02116
Phone: (617) 372-0965

#123
GEM
Category: Lounge, Italian
Average price: Expensive
Area: Downtown
Address: 42 Province St
Boston, MA 02108
Phone: (617) 482-1213

#124
T's Pub
Category: Bar, American
Average price: Modest
Area: Allston/Brighton
Address: 973 Commonwealth Ave
Boston, MA 02215
Phone: (617) 254-0807

#125
Orpheum Theatre
Category: Music Venues
Average price: Modest
Area: Downtown
Address: 1 Hamilton Pl
Boston, MA 02108
Phone: (617) 482-0106

#126
Atlantic Beer Garden
Category: American, Bar
Average price: Modest
Area: Waterfront, South Boston
Address: 146 Northern Ave
Boston, MA 02110
Phone: (617) 357-8000

#127
Lir Irish Pub & Restaurant
Category:Pub, Breakfast & Brunch
Average price: Modest
Area: Back Bay
Address: 903 Boylston St
Boston, MA 02115
Phone: (617) 778-0089

#128
Parla
Category: Italian, Cocktail Bar
Average price: Expensive
Area: North End
Address: 230 Hanover St
Boston, MA 02113
Phone: (617) 367-2824

#129
West End Johnnies
Category: American, Dance Club
Average price: Modest
Area: Downtown
Address: 138 Portland St
Boston, MA 02114
Phone: (617) 227-1588

#130
Villa Francesca
Category: Italian, Wine Bar
Average price: Expensive
Area: North End
Address: 150 Richmond St
Boston, MA 02109
Phone: (617) 367-2948

#131
Cuffs
Category: Irish, Bar
Average price: Modest
Area: Back Bay
Address: 350 Stuart St
Boston, MA 02116
Phone: (617) 532-3828

#132
Itadaki
Category: Japanese, Sushi Bar, Bar
Average price: Modest
Area: Back Bay
Address: 269 Newbury St
Boston, MA 02116
Phone: (617) 267-0840

#133
District
Category: Lounge, Tapas Bar
Average price: Expensive
Area: Waterfront, Leather District
Address: 180 Lincoln St
Boston, MA 02111
Phone: (617) 426-0180

#134
Tamo Bar
Category: Bar, American
Average price: Modest
Area: Downtown
Address: 1 Seaport Ln
Boston, MA 02228
Phone: (617) 385-4315

#135
The Boston Eagle
Category: Gay Bar
Average price: Inexpensive
Area: South End
Address: 520 Tremont St
Boston, MA 02116
Phone: (617) 542-4494

#136
Warehouse Bar & Grille
Category: Sports Bar, American
Average price: Modest
Area: Financial District
Address: 40 Broad St
Boston, MA 02109
Phone: (617) 936-4383

#137
The Shannon Tavern
Category: Bar, American
Average price: Modest
Area: South Boston
Address: 558 E 3rd St
Boston, MA 02127
Phone: (617) 269-9460

#138
The Clock Tavern
Category: Bar
Area: South Boston
Address: 342 W Broadway
Boston, MA 02127
Phone: (617) 269-2480

#139
South Boston Bowlarama
Category: Bowling, Bar
Average price: Inexpensive
Area: South Boston
Address: 543 E Broadway
Boston, MA 02127
Phone: (617) 464-4858

#140
Coda
Category: American, Bar
Average price: Modest
Area: Back Bay
Address: 329 Columbus Ave
Boston, MA 02116
Phone: (617) 536-2632

#141
**The Cornerstone
Restaurant & Pub**
Category: Pub, American
Average price: Inexpensive
Area: South Boston
Address: 16 W Broadway
Boston, MA 02127
Phone: (617) 269-9553

#142
Legal C Bar
Category: Seafood, Bar
Average price: Modest
Area: East Boston
Address: 1 Harborside Dr
Boston, MA 02128
Phone: (857) 241-2000

#143
Tiki Hideaway
Category: Bar
Average price: Modest
Area: Fenway
Address: 1271 Boylston St
Boston, MA 02215
Phone: (617) 267-3100

#144
Whiskey Priest
Category: Pub
Average price: Modest
Area: Waterfront, South Boston
Address: 150 Northern Ave
Boston, MA 02210
Phone: (617) 426-8111

#145
Venom
Category: Lounge
Average price: Modest
Area: Back Bay
Address: 384 Boylston St
Boston, MA 02228
Phone: (617) 859-8555

#146
Central Wharf
Category: Bar
Average price: Modest
Area: Financial District
Address: 160 Milk St
Boston, MA 02109
Phone: (617) 451-9460

#147
The Black Rose
Category: Pub, American
Average price: Modest
Area: Financial District
Address: 160 State St
Boston, MA 02109
Phone: (617) 742-2286

#148
M.C. Spiedo
Category: Italian, Lounge
Average price: Expensive
Area: Waterfront, South Boston
Address: 606 Congress St
Boston, MA 02210
Phone: (617) 476-5606

#149
El Kiosco Restaurant
Category: Latin American, Bar
Average price: Modest
Area: East Boston
Address: 972 Saratoga St
Boston, MA 02128
Phone: (617) 561-0101

#150
Boston Beer Garden
Category: Restaurant, Bar
Average price: Modest
Area: South Boston
Address: 734 E Broadway
Boston, MA 02127
Phone: (617) 269-0990

#151
Tia's On the Waterfront
Category: Seafood, Cocktail Bar
Average price: Modest
Area: Waterfront
Address: 200 Atlantic Ave
Boston, MA 02110
Phone: (617) 227-0828

#152
Community Music Center of Boston
Category: Music Venues
Area: South End
Address: 34 Warren Ave
Boston, MA 02116
Phone: (617) 482-7494

#153
AIC Boston Center
Category: Venues, Event Space,
Music Venues, Art Gallery
Average price: Modest
Area: Back Bay
Address: 38 Newbury St
Boston, MA 02116
Phone: (617) 266-0080

#154
Savvor Restaurant and Lounge
Category: Lounge, American
Average price: Modest
Area: Waterfront, Leather District
Address: 180 Lincoln St
Boston, MA 02111
Phone: (857) 250-2165

#155
Splash Ultra Lounge & Burger Bar
Category: Lounge, Burgers
Average price: Modest
Area: Waterfront, Leather District
Address: 150 Kneeland St
Boston, MA 02111
Phone: (617) 426-6397

#156
Market
Category: Lounge, American
Average price: Modest
Area: Financial District
Address: 21 Broad St
Boston, MA 02109
Phone: (617) 263-0037

#157
Liquor Store
Category: Dance Club, Bar
Average price: Modest
Area: Back Bay
Address: 25 Boylston Pl
Boston, MA 02116
Phone: (617) 357-6800

#158
Sidebar Food & Spirits
Category: American, Dive Bar, Pub
Average price: Inexpensive
Area: Downtown
Address: 14 Bromfield St
Boston, MA 02108
Phone: (617) 357-1899

#159
M.J. O'Connor's
Category: Pub, American
Average price: Modest
Area: South Boston
Address: 425 Summer St
Boston, MA 02210
Phone: (617) 443-0800

#160
Boston Fun Cruises
Category: Tour, Jazz & Blues
Average price: Inexpensive
Area: Waterfront, South Boston
Address: 88 Sleeper St
Boston, MA 02210
Phone: (617) 821-6127

#161
Sports Connection Bar & Grill
Category: Sports Bar
Average price: Inexpensive
Area: South Boston
Address: 560 Dorchester Ave
Boston, MA 02127
Phone: (617) 268-4119

#162
The Dot Tavern
Category: Bar
Average price: Inexpensive
Area: Dorchester
Address: 840 Dorchester Ave
Boston, MA 02125
Phone: (617) 288-6288

#163
The Reef
Category: Bar, American
Average price: Modest
Area: Waterfront
Address: 1 Central Wharf
Boston, MA 02110
Phone: (617) 973-0234

#164
Copperfield's Bar
& Down Under Pub
Category: Bar, Music Venues
Average price: Modest
Area: Fenway
Address: 98 Brookline Ave
Boston, MA 02215
Phone: (617) 247-8605

#165
Ristorante Fiore
Category: Italian, Wine Bar
Average price: Expensive
Area: North End
Address: 250 Hanover St
Boston, MA 02113
Phone: (617) 371-1176

#166
Mojitos Latin Lounge & Nightclub
Category: Bar, Dance Club, Colombian
Average price: Modest
Area: Downtown
Address: 48 Winter St
Boston, MA 02108
Phone: (617) 834-0552

#167
SideBar & Grille
Category: Chicken Wings, Lounge
Average price: Modest
Area: Back Bay
Address: 39 Dalton Street
Boston, MA 02199
Phone: (617) 236-2000

#168
The Bar Room
Category: Pub, Dance Club
Average price: Modest
Area: Financial District
Address: 5 Broad St
Boston, MA 02228
Phone: (617) 723-7877

#169
City Bar
Category: Lounge
Average price: Modest
Area: South Boston
Address: 425 Summer St
Boston, MA 02210
Phone: (617) 532-4600

#170
Daisy Buchanan's
Category: Bar
Average price: Modest
Area: Back Bay
Address: 240A Newbury St
Boston, MA 02116
Phone: (617) 247-8516

#171
Bijou
Category: Dance Club, Lounge
Average price: Expensive
Area: Chinatown
Address: 51 Stuart St
Boston, MA 02116
Phone: (617) 357-4565

#172
Victory Pub
Category: Pub
Average price: Inexpensive
Area: East Boston
Address: 1004 Bennington St
Boston, MA 02128
Phone: (617) 561-0991

#173
Touchie's Shamrock Pub
Category: Pub
Average price: Inexpensive
Area: South Boston
Address: 501 E 8th St
Boston, MA 02127
Phone: (617) 268-0007

#174
Back Bay Events Center
Category: Performing Arts,
Music Venues
Area: Back Bay
Address: 180 Berkeley St
Boston, MA 02116
Phone: (617) 236-1199

#175
The Rattlesnake Bar & Grill
Category: Bar, American
Average price: Modest
Area: Back Bay
Address: 384 Boylston St
Boston, MA 02116
Phone: (617) 859-8555

#176
Bar 1221
Category: Bar, Beer, Wine, Spirits
Area: Back Bay
Address: 699 Boylston at Exeter
Boston, MA 02455
Phone: (617) 266-5858

#177
Tavern In the Square
Category: Sandwiches, Bar
Average price: Modest
Area: Waterfront, South Boston
Address: 640 Atlantic Ave
Boston, MA 02111
Phone: (857) 233-4717

#178
William's Tavern
Category: Dive Bar
Average price: Inexpensive
Area: South Boston
Address: 92 A St
Boston, MA 02127
Phone: (617) 269-9646

#179
The Alley Bar
Category: Bar
Average price: Exclusive
Area: Financial District
Address: 70 Rowes Wharf
Boston, MA 02110
Phone: (617) 748-1857

#180
Caprice
Category: Lounge, American
Average price: Modest
Area: Back Bay
Address: 275 Tremont St
Boston, MA 02116
Phone: (617) 292-0080

#181
The Terrace
Category: Lounge
Area: North End
Address: 3 Battery Wharf
Boston, MA 02109
Phone: (617) 994-9000

#182
Julep Bar
Category: American, Lounge
Average price: Modest
Area: Financial District
Address: 200 High St
Boston, MA 02110
Phone: (617) 261-4200

#183
Tequila Rain
Category: Dance Club
Average price: Modest
Area: Fenway
Address: 145 Ipswich St
Boston, MA 02215
Phone: (617) 859-0030

#184
Lucky's Lounge
Category: Lounge, Fast Food
Average price: Modest
Area: East Boston
Address: 12 Harborside Dr
Boston, MA 02128
Phone: (617) 567-2299

#185
Boston Beerworks Pier B
Average price: Modest
Area: East Boston
Address: 18 B Logan Airport
Boston, MA 02128
Phone: (617) 569-2277

#186
Matrix
Category: Dance Club
Area: Back Bay
Address: 275 Tremont St
Boston, MA 02116
Phone: (617) 542-4077

#187
Bar Louie
Category: Bar, American
Average price: Modest
Area: Fenway
Address: 121 Brookline Ave
Boston, MA 02215
Phone: (617) 449-7010

#188
Laugh Boston
Category: Comedy Club
Average price: Modest
Area: South Boston
Address: 425 Summer St
Boston, MA 02210
Phone: (617) 725-2844

#189
The Glass Slipper
Category: Adult Entertainment
Average price: Expensive
Area: Chinatown
Address: 22 Lagrange St
Boston, MA 02116
Phone: (617) 338-2290

#190
Four Winds Bar and Grill
Category: Bar, Karaoke
Area: North End
Address: 266 Commercial St
Boston, MA 02109
Phone: (617) 742-3922

#191
Harborside Lounge
Category: Lounge
Average price: Expensive
Area: Financial District
Address: 185 State St
Boston, MA 02109
Phone: (617) 723-7500

#192
Who's On First
Category: Sports Bar
Average price: Modest
Area: Fenway
Address: 19 Yawkey Way
Boston, MA 02215
Phone: (617) 247-3353

#193
Machine
Category: Gay Bar
Average price: Modest
Area: Fenway
Address: 1256 Boylston St
Boston, MA 02215
Phone: (617) 536-1950

#194
Centerfolds
Category: Adult Entertainment, Bar
Average price: Expensive
Area: Chinatown
Address: 12 Lagrange St
Boston, MA 02116
Phone: (617) 292-2600

#195
Delux Café
Category: Bar, American
Average price: Modest
Area: South End
Address: 100 Chandler St
Boston, MA 02116
Phone: (617) 338-5258

#196
Dick Doherty's Comedy Den
Category: Performing Arts, Comedy Club
Average price: Modest
Area: Financial District
Address: 184 High St
Boston, MA 02110
Phone: (800) 401-2221

#197
Trophy Room
Category: Sports Bar, American
Average price: Modest
Area: South End
Address: 26 Chandler St
Boston, MA 02116
Phone: (617) 482-3450

#198
The Place
Category: Restaurant, Sports Bar
Average price: Modest
Area: Financial District
Address: 2 Broad St
Boston, MA 02109
Phone: (617) 523-2081

#199
Volle Nolle
Category: Wine Bar, American,
Tapas/Small Plates
Average price: Modest
Area: North End
Address: 351 Hanover St
Boston, MA 02113
Phone: (617) 523-0003

#200
Boston Chops
Category: Bar, Steakhouse
Average price: Expensive
Area: South End
Address: 1375 Washington St
Boston, MA 02118
Phone: (617) 227-5011

#201
Capiz Bar
Category: Bar
Average price: Modest
Area: Waterfront, South Boston
Address: 606 Congress St
Boston, MA 02210
Phone: (617) 338-4111

#202
Greater Boston House Concerts
Category: Music Venues
Area: Dorchester
Address: 21 Virginia St
Boston, MA 02125
Phone: (617) 947-1330

#203
North 26 Restaurant & Bar
Category: Bar, Breakfast & Brunch
Area: South Boston
Address: 26 N St
Boston, MA 02109
Phone: (617) 523-3600

#204
Three Cheers Restaurant Bar
& Function Facility
Category: American, Sports Bar
Area: Waterfront, South Boston
Address: 290 Congress St
Boston, MA 02210
Phone: (617) 423-2438

#205
The Tank
Category: Dance Club, Adult Entertainment
Average price: Expensive
Area: Allston/Brighton
Address: 277 Babcock St
Boston, MA 02215
Phone: (857) 294-3122

#206
Allston Billiards
Category: Pool Hall
Area: Allston/Brighton
Address: 445 Cambridge St
Boston, MA 02134
Phone: (617) 782-0969

#207
The Golden Leaf Karaoke
Category: Karaoke
Average price: Modest
Area: Chinatown
Address: 20 Hudson St
Boston, MA 02111
Phone: (617) 988-8188

#208
Opal Lounge
Category: Lounge
Area: Downtown
Address: 48 Winter St
Boston, MA 02108
Phone: (617) 482-6725

#209
An Tain
Category: Dive Bar
Average price: Inexpensive
Area: Financial District
Address: 31 India St
Boston, MA 02110
Phone: (617) 426-1870

#210
Blue Wave
Category: Bar
Average price: Modest
Area: Waterfront, South Boston
Address: 343 Congress St
Boston, MA 02210
Phone: (617) 790-0720

#211
St. Mark's Post
Category: Dive Bar, Karaoke, Pool Hall
Area: Dorchester
Address: 69 Bailey St
Boston, MA 02124
Phone: (617) 436-8939

#212
Arc Nightclub
Category: Dance Club, Lounge
Average price: Modest
Area: Fenway
Address: 835 Beacon St
Boston, MA 02215
Phone: (857) 350-3799

#213
Teranga
Category: Bar, Senegalese
Average price: Modest
Area: South End
Address: 1746 Washington St
Boston, MA 02118
Phone: (617) 266-0003

#214
Boston Beer Works
Category: Bar, Breakfast & Brunch,
Sandwiches, Beer, Wine, Spirits
Average price: Modest
Area: East Boston
Address: 1 Harborside Dr
Boston, MA 02128
Phone: (617) 569-2277

#215
Trainor's Cafe
Category: Bar, American
Area: East Boston
Address: 127 Maverick St
Boston, MA 02128
Phone: (617) 567-6995

#216
Sip Wine Bar and Kitchen
Category: Wine Bar
Average price: Modest
Area: Chinatown
Address: 581 Washington St
Boston, MA 02111
Phone: (617) 956-0888

#217
O'Brian's Pub
Category: American, Pub
Area: East Boston
Address: 1 Harborside Dr
Boston, MA 02128
Phone: (617) 561-0093

#218
Precinct Kitchen + Bar
Category: Bar, American
Average price: Modest
Area: Back Bay
Address: 154 Berkeley St
Boston, MA 02116
Phone: (617) 532-3827

#219
Minibar Boston
Category: Lounge
Area: Back Bay
Address: 51 Huntington Ave
Boston, MA 02116
Phone: (617) 424-8500

#220
El Bembe
Category: Dance Club
Area: South End
Address: 85 West Newton Street
Boston, MA 02118
Phone: (617) 927-1730

#221
Seapoint Restaurant
Category: Bar, American
Average price: Modest
Area: South Boston
Address: 367 E 8th St
Boston, MA 02127
Phone: (617) 268-1476

#222
Rock On! Concert Cruises
Category: Music Venues
Area: Waterfront
Address: 60 Rowes Wharf
Boston, MA 02210
Phone: (617) 544-7625

#223
afterHours
Category: Music Venues
Average price: Inexpensive
Area: Fenway
Address: 360 Huntington Avenue
Boston, MA 02115
Phone: (617) 373-2642

#224
Down Ultra Lounge
Category: Lounge, Dance Club
Average price: Modest
Area: Financial District
Address: 184 High St
Boston, MA 02110
Phone: (617) 292-4699

#225
Sonsie
Category: American, Wine Bar
Average price: Expensive
Area: Back Bay
Address: 327 Newbury St
Boston, MA 02115
Phone: (617) 351-2500

#226
Club Acela
Category: Lounge
Area: Waterfront, South Boston
Address: 2 S Station St
Boston, MA 02111
Phone: (617) 757-1520

#227
Centre Bar
Category: Bar
Average price: Inexpensive
Area: Dorchester
Address: 1664 Dorchester Ave
Boston, MA 02122
Phone: (617) 436-0700

#228
BarLola Tapas Lounge
Category: Tapas Bar, Lounge
Average price: Modest
Area: Back Bay
Address: 160 Commonwealth Ave
Boston, MA 02228
Phone: (617) 266-1122

#229
City Lights Cruises
Category: Boat Charters, Dance Club
Average price: Modest
Area: Waterfront
Address: Rowes Wharf
Boston, MA 02110
Phone: (212) 822-8880

#230
Plaza Theatres
at Boston Center for the Arts
Category: Performing Arts, Music Venues
Area: South End
Address: 539 Tremont St
Boston, MA 02116
Phone: (617) 426-5000

#231
Connexion Lounge
Category: Lounge
Average price: Modest
Area: Back Bay
Address: 110 Huntington Ave
Boston, MA 02116
Phone: (617) 236-5800

#232
Metropolis Cafe
Category: Wine Bar, Mediterranean
Average price: Modest
Area: South End
Address: 584 Tremont St
Boston, MA 02118
Phone: (617) 247-2931

#233
Coco's Bar & Lounge
Category: Bar, Latin American
Area: Egleston Square, Jamaica Plain
Address: 3171 Washington St
Boston, MA 02130
Phone: (617) 522-7500

#234
Melange at District
Category: Gay Bar, Karaoke
Average price: Expensive
Area: Waterfront, Leather District
Address: 180 Lincoln St
Boston, MA 02111
Phone: (617) 417-0186

#235
BU Central
Category: Music Venues
Area: Allston/Brighton
Address: 775 Commonwealth Ave
Boston, MA 02215
Phone: (617) 353-3635

#236
Taverna Medallo
Category: Bar
Area: East Boston
Address: 411 Chelsea St
Boston, MA 02128
Phone: (617) 567-2727

#237
Bull & Finch Enterprises
Category: Pub
Area: Beacon Hill
Address: 84 Beacon St
Boston, MA 02108
Phone: (617) 227-9605

#238
Pockets Billiard Club
Category: Pool Hall
Average price: Inexpensive
Area: East Boston
Address: 981 Bennington Street
Boston, MA 02128
Phone: (617) 569-3350

#239
Van Shabu & Bar
Category: Japanese, Bar, Sushi Bar
Average price: Modest
Area: Dorchester
Address: 1156 Dorchester Ave
Boston, MA 02125
Phone: (617) 436-8100

#240
Market Lounge
Category: Nightlife
Average price: Expensive
Area: Financial District
Address: 120 Water St
Boston, MA 02109
Phone: (617) 367-0658

#241
Jin Karaoke
Category: Karaoke
Area: Allston/Brighton
Address: 16 Harvard Ave
Boston, MA 02134
Phone: (617) 782-9282

#242
Club Q
Category: Nightlife
Area: Downtown
Address: 25 Union Street
Boston, MA 02228
Phone: (857) 829-3766

#243
Logan's Lounge
Category: Nightlife
Area: East Boston
Address: 276 Bennington Street
Boston, MA 02128
Phone: (617) 569-6167

#244
Jazz in the Air
Category: Musicians, Jazz & Blues
Area: Fenway
Address: St Marys St
Boston, MA 02115
Phone: (978) 898-4975

#245
Blazing Paddles
Category: Sports Bar
Area: Fenway
Address: 82 Lansdowne St
Boston, MA 02115
Phone: (617) 351-7001

#246
Pony Lounge
Category: Nightlife
Area: East Boston
Address: 411 Chelsea St
Boston, MA 02128
Phone: (617) 567-9775

#247
Superstition
Area: Fenway
Address: 835 Beacon St
Boston, MA 02215
Phone: (617) 262-2121

#248
Jerry Remy's Sports Bar & Grill
Category: American, Sports Bar
Average price: Modest
Area: Waterfront, South Boston
Address: 250 Northern Ave
Boston, MA 02210
Phone: (617) 856-7369

#249
Boston Male Strippers
Category: Adult Entertainment
Average price: Modest
Area: Back Bay
Address: 100 Huntington Ave
Boston, MA 02116
Phone: (866) 404-4401

#250
The Gallery
Category: Tea Rooms, Lounge
Area: Chinatown
Address: 2 Avery St
Boston, MA 02111
Phone: (617) 574-7100

#251
Finch
Area: Downtown
Address: 107 Merrimac St
Boston, MA 02114
Phone: (617) 624-0202

#252
Celebrity Series of Boston
Area: Back Bay
Address: 20 Park Plz
Boston, MA 02116
Phone: (617) 482-2595

#253
Bijou
Area: Back Bay
Address: 100 Huntington Ave
Boston, MA 02116
Phone: (617) 267-1209

#254
Red Lantern Club
Area: Back Bay
Address: 710 Boylston St
Boston, MA 02228
Phone: (617) 262-3900

#255
Guilded Boston
Area: Back Bay
Address: 213 Newbury Street
Boston, MA 02116
Phone: (617) 429-8968

#256
Four-Handed Illusions: An Intimate Evening of Laughs and Wonder
Category: Performing Arts, Comedy Club
Average price: Modest
Area: Beacon Hill
Address: 84 Beacon St
Boston, MA 02108
Phone: (781) 850-6924

#257
Chris Harris Presents
Area: South Boston
Address: 1 Boylston Pl
Boston, MA 02118
Phone: (401) 559-3489

#258
Musica Vesuviana Italy Music Camp
Category: Summer Camp, Music Venues
Area: Back Bay
Address: 651 Boylston St
Boston, MA 02116
Phone: (339) 707-3593

#259
Opera On Tap Boston
Category: Pub, Piano Bar
Area: Chinatown
Address: 37 Stuart St
Boston, MA 02116
Phone: (617) 338-8586

#260
Keros Entertainment
Area: Back Bay
Address: 110 Beacon St
Boston, MA 02215
Phone: (617) 487-8807

#261
Jazz Bands - Boston
Area: South End
Address: 131 West Concord St.
Boston, MA 02118
Phone: (617) 312-3554

#262
JG & The MeggaTones
Area: Downtown
Address: 449 Washington St
Boston, MA 02111
Phone: (617) 799-9033

#263
Joy Street Pub
Area: Beacon Hill
Address: 60 Joy St
Boston, MA 02114
Phone: (617) 723-4656

#264
360 Ultra Lounge
Area: Financial District
Address: 35 Batterymarch St
Boston, MA 02109
Phone: (617) 695-9333

#265
Mr Dooleys Irish Pub
Area: Financial District
Address: 77 Broad St
Boston, MA 02109
Phone: (617) 338-5656

#266
Aga's Highland Tap
Area: Dudley Square
Address: 2128 Washington St
Boston, MA 02119
Phone: (617) 427-6514

#267
Great Boston Experience
Area: South Boston
Address: 244 W 3rd St
Boston, MA 02127
Phone: (855) 262-3377

#268
M.J. O'Connor's
Area: South Boston
Address: 425 Summer St
Boston, MA 02210
Phone: (617) 443-0800

#269
Applebees Neighborhood Grill & Bar
Category: Bar
Area: Dorchester
Address: 11 Allstate Rd
Boston, MA 02125
Phone: (617) 442-7139

#270
Aragosta Bar & Bistro
Area: North End
Address: 377 Commercial St
Boston, MA 02109
Phone: (617) 994-9001

#271
Sexy Boston Strippers
Area: Charlestown
Address: 86 Main St
Boston, MA 02129
Phone: (866) 569-6980

#272
Bachelor Party Headquarters
Area: Charlestown
Address: 89 Main St
Boston, MA 02129
Phone: (617) 772-0200

#273
Billares Colombia
Area: East Boston
Address: 28 Bennington St
Boston, MA 02128
Phone: (617) 569-5740

#274
Condor Street Studio
Category: Music Venues,
Recording & Rehearsal Studio
Area: East Boston
Address: 100 Condor St
Boston, MA 02128
Phone: (617) 444-9532

#275
Mike Davidson Recording
Area: Allston/Brighton
Address: 52 Everett St
Boston, MA 02134
Phone: (800) 846-5495

#276
Lower Mills Pub
Category: Dive Bar, Pub, Sports Bar
Average price: Modest
Area: Dorchester
Address: 2269 Dorchester Ave
Boston, MA 02124
Phone: (617) 322-9721

#277
Cisco Brew Pub
Category: Bar
Average price: Modest
Area: East Boston
Address: 1 Harborside Dr
Boston, MA 02128
Phone: (617) 561-8782

#278
Kiosco Sabor De Mi Tierra Bar
Area: East Boston
Address: 972 Saratoga St
Boston, MA 02128
Phone: (617) 567-7293

#279
Limoncello Ristorante
Category: Italian, Wine Bar
Average price: Expensive
Area: North End
Address: 190 N St
Boston, MA 02127
Phone: (617) 523-4480

#280
Legal Harborside
Category: Seafood, American, Wine Bar
Average price: Expensive
Area: Waterfront, South Boston
Address: 270 Northern Ave
Boston, MA 02210
Phone: (617) 477-2900

#281
The Druid
Category: Pub, Irish, American
Average price: Modest
Area: Inman Square
Address: 1357 Cambridge St
Cambridge, MA 02139
Phone: (617) 497-0965

#282
Navy Yard Bistro & Wine Bar
Category: Wine Bar, American
Average price: Expensive
Area: Charlestown
Address: 6th St
Charlestown, MA 02129
Phone: (617) 242-0036

#283
Deep Ellum
Category: Pub, Breakfast & Brunch
Average price: Modest
Area: Allston/Brighton
Address: 477 Cambridge St
Allston, MA 02134
Phone: (617) 787-2337

#284
Stanza Dei Sigari
Category: Tobacco Shop,
Lounge, Hookah Bar
Average price: Expensive
Area: North End
Address: 292 Hanover St
Boston, MA 02113
Phone: (617) 227-0295

#285
City Table
Category: Bar, American
Average price: Modest
Area: Back Bay
Address: 61 Exeter St
Boston, MA 02116
Phone: (617) 933-4800

#286
Green Street
Category: Lounge, American
Average price: Modest
Area: Central Square
Address: 280 Green St
Cambridge, MA 02139
Phone: (617) 876-1655

#287
Brendan Behan Pub
Category: Pub
Average price: Inexpensive
Area: Jamaica Plain
Address: 378 Centre St
Jamaica Plain, MA 02130
Phone: (617) 522-5386

#288
Sunset Grill & Tap
Category: Bar, American
Average price: Modest
Area: Allston/Brighton
Address: 130 Brighton Ave
Allston, MA 02134
Phone: (617) 254-1331

#289
West Bridge
Category: Bar, American, French
Average price: Expensive
Area: Kendall Square/MIT
Address: 1 Kendall Sq
Cambridge, MA 02141
Phone: (617) 945-0221

#290
Tres Gatos
Category: Tapas Bar, Wine Bar
Average price: Modest
Area: Jamaica Plain
Address: 470 Centre St
Jamaica Plain, MA 02130
Phone: (617) 477-4851

#291
Club Passim
Category: Music Venues
Average price: Modest
Area: Harvard Square
Address: 47 Palmer St
Cambridge, MA 02138
Phone: (617) 492-7679

#292
The Plough & Stars
Category: Music Venues, Irish
Average price: Modest
Area: Central Square
Address: 912 Massachusetts Ave
Cambridge, MA 02139
Phone: (617) 576-0032

#293
PARK Restaurant & Bar
Category: American, Bar
Average price: Modest
Area: Harvard Square
Address: 59 JFK St
Cambridge, MA 02138
Phone: (617) 491-9851

#294
Oberon
Category: Performing Arts, Bar
Average price: Modest
Area: Harvard Square
Address: 2 Arrow St
Cambridge, MA 02138
Phone: (617) 496-8004

#295
Lizard Lounge
Category: Music Venues, Burgers
Average price: Modest
Area: Porter Square
Address: 1667 Massachusetts Ave
Cambridge, MA 02138
Phone: (617) 547-0759

#296
Newtowne Grille
Category: Pizza, Pub, American
Average price: Inexpensive
Area: Porter Square
Address: 1945 Massachusetts Ave
Cambridge, MA 02140
Phone: (617) 661-0706

#297
The Muddy Charles Pub at MIT
Category: Pub
Average price: Inexpensive
Area: Kendall Square/MIT
Address: 142 Memorial Dr
Cambridge, MA 02139
Phone: (617) 253-2086

#298
Toad
Category: Dance Club, Dive Bar
Average price: Inexpensive
Area: Porter Square
Address: 1912 Massachusetts Ave
Cambridge, MA 02140
Phone: (617) 497-4950

#299
The Squealing Pig
Category: Pub, Irish
Average price: Modest
Area: Mission Hill
Address: 134 Smith St
Roxbury Crossing, MA 02120
Phone: (617) 566-6651

#300
Belly Wine Bar
Category: Wine Bar
Average price: Modest
Area: Kendall Square/MIT
Address: One Kendall Square
Cambridge, MA 02139
Phone: (617) 494-0968

#301
Puritan & Company
Category: American, Cocktail Bar
Average price: Expensive
Area: Inman Square
Address: 1166 Cambridge St
Cambridge, MA 02139
Phone: (617) 615-6195

#302
The Comedy Studio
Category: Comedy Club
Average price: Inexpensive
Area: Harvard Square
Address: 1238 Massachusetts Ave
Cambridge, MA 02138
Phone: (617) 661-6507

#303
Whiskey's Food & Spirits
Category: Bar, American
Average price: Modest
Area: Back Bay
Address: 885 Boylston St
Boston, MA 02116
Phone: (617) 262-5551

#304
Great Scott
Category: Dance Club, Lounge,
Music Venues
Average price: Inexpensive
Area: Allston/Brighton
Address: 1222 Commonwealth Ave
Allston, MA 02134
Phone: (617) 566-9014

#305
The Banshee
Category: Pub, Irish
Average price: Modest
Area: Dorchester
Address: 934 Dorchester Ave
Dorchester, MA 02125
Phone: (617) 436-9747

#306
Shays Pub & Wine Bar
Category: American, Wine Bar, Pub
Average price: Modest
Area: Harvard Square
Address: 58 JFK St
Cambridge, MA 02138
Phone: (617) 864-9161

#307
Porter Cafe
Category: Pub
Average price: Modest
Area: West Roxbury Center, West Roxbury
Address: 1723 Centre St
West Roxbury, MA 02132
Phone: (617) 942-2579

#308
The Regal Beagle
Category: Bar, Breakfast & Brunch
Average price: Modest
Area: Coolidge Corner
Address: 308 Harvard St
Brookline, MA 02446
Phone: (617) 739-5151

#309
Istanbul'lu
Category: Turkish, Wine Bar
Average price: Modest
Area: Teele Square
Address: 237 Holland St
Somerville, MA 02144
Phone: (617) 440-7387

#310
Havana Club
Category: Dance Club
Average price: Modest
Area: Central Square
Address: 288 Green St
Cambridge, MA 02138
Phone: (617) 312-5550

#311
Matt Murphy's Pub
Category: Pub, Irish
Average price: Modest
Area: Brookline Village
Address: 14 Harvard St
Brookline, MA 02445
Phone: (617) 232-0188

#312
DBAR
Category: Dance Club, American
Average price: Modest
Area: Dorchester
Address: 1236 Dorchester Ave
Dorchester, MA 02125
Phone: (617) 265-4490

#313
The Field
Category: Pub, Burgers, Sandwiches
Average price: Inexpensive
Area: Central Square
Address: 20 Prospect St
Cambridge, MA 02139
Phone: (617) 354-7345

#314
People's Republik
Category: Bar
Average price: Inexpensive
Area: Central Square
Address: 876-878 Massachusetts Ave
Cambridge, MA 02139
Phone: (617) 491-6969

#315
Trophy Room
Area: South End
Address: 26 Chandler St
Boston, MA 02116
Phone: (617) 482-3450

#316
Neighborhood Arts
Area: South End
Address: 34 Warren Ave
Boston, MA 02116
Phone: (617) 482-7494

#317
Grill 23 & Bar
Category: Steakhouse, Wine Bar
Average price: Exclusive
Area: Back Bay
Address: 161 Berkeley St
Boston, MA 02116
Phone: (617) 542-2255

#318
City Bar
Area: Back Bay
Address: 65 Exeter St
Boston, MA 02116
Phone: (617) 933-4801

#319
Creative Connections
Area: Back Bay
Address: 172 Newbury St
Boston, MA 02116
Phone: (617) 236-6996

#320
711
Area: Back Bay
Address: 711 Boylston St
Boston, MA 02116
Phone: (617) 236-1777

#321
Cambridge Common
Category: American, Bar
Average price: Modest
Area: Porter Square
Address: 1667 Massachusetts Ave
Cambridge, MA 02138
Phone: (617) 547-1228

#322
Monday Afternoon Inc
Area: Beacon Hill
Address: 149 Charles St
Boston, MA 02114
Phone: (617) 523-1895

#323
Rum Ba
Area: Waterfront, South Boston
Address: 510 Atlantic Ave
Boston, MA 02210
Phone: (617) 217-5152

#324
The Party Music Masters
Area: Financial District
Address: 265 Franklin St
Boston, MA 02110
Phone: (781) 871-2701

#325
City Cafe
Area: Financial District
Address: 274 Franklin St
Boston, MA 02110
Phone: (617) 261-7458

#326
Silhouette Lounge
Category: Dive Bar, Lounge
Average price: Inexpensive
Area: Allston/Brighton
Address: 200 Brighton Ave
Allston, MA 02134
Phone: (617) 206-4565

#327
Caliterra Bar & Grille
Area: Financial District
Address: 89 Broad St
Boston, MA 02110
Phone: (617) 556-0006

#328
Couture44
Area: Downtown
Address: 52 Temple St.
Boston, MA 02228
Phone: (617) 990-4824

#329
West Side Lounge
Category: Lounge, American
Average price: Modest
Area: Porter Square
Address: 1680 Massachusetts Ave
Cambridge, MA 02138
Phone: (617) 441-5566

#330
Thats Entertainment
Area: Fenway
Address: 7 Lansdowne St
Boston, MA 02215
Phone: (617) 262-2424

#331
7 Lansdowne Street Embassy
Area: Fenway
Address: 41 Lansdowne St
Boston, MA 02215
Phone: (617) 536-2100

#332
ArtsBoston
Area: Dudley Square
Address: 31 St. James St
Boston, MA 02116
Phone: (617) 262-8632

#333
Temple Bar
Category: American, Bar
Average price: Modest
Area: Porter Square
Address: 1688 Massachusetts Ave
Cambridge, MA 02138
Phone: (617) 547-5055

#334
Treading the Boston
Atheletic Club
Area: South Boston
Address: 653 Summer St Ste 1
Boston, MA 02210
Phone: (617) 464-7984

#335
Cantab Lounge
Category: Lounge, Music Venues
Average price: Inexpensive
Area: Central Square
Address: 738 Massachusetts Ave
Cambridge, MA 02139
Phone: (617) 354-2685

#336
New England Strippers
Area: Charlestown
Address: 123 Main St
Boston, MA 02129
Phone: (877) 847-1904

#337
The Warren Tavern
Category: Bar, American
Average price: Modest
Area: Charlestown
Address: 2 Pleasant St
Charlestown, MA 02129
Phone: (617) 241-8142

#338
Tavern at the End of the World
Category: Pub, American
Average price: Modest
Area: Charlestown
Address: 108 Cambridge St
Charlestown, MA 02129
Phone: (617) 241-4999

#339
El Poder Musical
Area: East Boston
Address: 153 Meridian St
Boston, MA 02128
Phone: (617) 567-4533

#340
The Middle East
Restaurant And Nightclub
Category: Middle Eastern, Music Venues
Average price: Modest
Area: Central Square
Address: 472 Massachusetts Ave
Cambridge, MA 02139
Phone: (617) 864-3278

#341
Harry's Bar & Grill
Category: Bar, American
Average price: Modest
Area: Allston/Brighton
Address: 1430 Commonwealth Ave
Brighton, MA 02135
Phone: (617) 738-9990

#342
Nile Lounge
Category: Lounge, Hookah Bar
Average price: Modest
Area: Allston/Brighton
Address: 70 Brighton Ave
Allston, MA 02134
Phone: (617) 202-3011

#343
Stoli Bar & Restaurant
Category: Russian, Lounge
Average price: Expensive
Area: Brookline Village
Address: 213 Washington St
Brookline, MA 02445
Phone: (617) 731-5070

#344
Johnny D's
Category: Bar, Music Venues
Average price: Modest
Area: Davis Square
Address: 17 Holland St
Somerville, MA 02144
Phone: (617) 776-2004

#345
Brick & Mortar
Category: Bar
Average price: Modest
Area: Central Square
Address: 567 Massachusetts Ave
Cambridge, MA 02139
Phone: (617) 491-0016

#346
James Gate
Category: Pub, American
Average price: Modest
Area: Jamaica Plain
Address: 5 McBride St
Jamaica Plain, MA 02130
Phone: (617) 983-2000

#347
Tremont 647
Category: Bar, American
Average price: Modest
Area: South End
Address: 647 Tremont St
Boston, MA 02118
Phone: (617) 266-4600

#348
Lord Hobo
Category: Bar, American
Average price: Modest
Area: Inman Square
Address: 92 Hampshire St
Cambridge, MA 02139
Phone: (617) 250-8454

#349
Club Cafe
Category: Gay Bar, Lounge
Average price: Modest
Area: Back Bay
Address: 209 Columbus Ave
Boston, MA 02116
Phone: (617) 536-0966

#350
Five Horses Tavern
Category: American, Pub
Average price: Modest
Area: Davis Square
Address: 400 Highland Ave
Somerville, MA 02144
Phone: (617) 764-1655

#351
Ecco
Category: American, Bar
Average price: Modest
Area: East Boston
Address: 107 Porter St East
Boston, MA 02128
Phone: (617) 561-1112

#352
TT the Bear's Place
Category: Bar, Music Venues
Average price: Inexpensive
Area: Central Square
Address: 10 Brookline St
Cambridge, MA 02139
Phone: (617) 492-0082

#353
The Cambridge Queen's Head
Category: Pub
Average price: Inexpensive
Area: Harvard Square
Address: 45 Quincy St
Cambridge, MA 02138
Phone: (617) 495-5107

#354
The Cellar
Category: American, Bar
Average price: Modest
Area: Central Square
Address: 991 Massachusetts Ave
Cambridge, MA 02138
Phone: (617) 876-2580

#355
Ryles
Category: Jazz & Blues, Music Venues
Average price: Modest
Area: Inman Square
Address: 212 Hampshire St
Cambridge, MA 02139
Phone: (617) 876-9330

#356
Meadhall
Category: Bar, American
Average price: Modest
Area: Kendall Square/MIT
Address: 4 Cambridge Ctr
Cambridge, MA 02142
Phone: (617) 714-4372

#357
Barlow's Restaurant
Category: Bar, American, Seafood
Average price: Modest
Area: Waterfront, South Boston
Address: 241 A St
Boston, MA 02210
Phone: (617) 338-2142

#358
Galway House
Category: Bar, Seafood
Average price: Modest
Area: Jamaica Plain
Address: 710 Centre St
Jamaica Plain, MA 02130
Phone: (617) 524-9677

#359
Saloon
Category: American, Pub
Average price: Modest
Area: Davis Square
Address: 255 Elm St
Somerville, MA 02144
Phone: (617) 628-4444

#360
Blarney Stone
Category: Bar, American
Average price: Modest
Area: Dorchester, Fields Corner
Address: 1509 Dorchester Ave
Dorchester, MA 02122
Phone: (617) 436-8223

#361
The Lily Pad
Category: Performing Arts,
Music Venues, Jazz & Blues
Average price: Inexpensive
Area: Inman Square
Address: 1353 Cambridge St
Cambridge, MA 02139
Phone: (617) 395-1393

#362
Hops N Scotch
Category: Bar
Average price: Modest
Area: Coolidge Corner
Address: 1306 Beacon St
Brookline, MA 02446
Phone: (617) 232-8808

#363
Noir
Category: Lounge, American
Average price: Modest
Area: Harvard Square
Address: 1 Bennett St
Cambridge, MA 02138
Phone: (617) 661-8010

#364
Midway Cafe
Category: Music Venues, Bar, Karaoke
Average price: Inexpensive
Area: Jamaica Plain
Address: 3496 Washington St
Jamaica Plain, MA 02130
Phone: (617) 524-9038

#365
Grafton Street
Category: American, Pub
Average price: Modest
Area: Harvard Square
Address: 1230 Massachusetts Ave
Cambridge, MA 02138
Phone: (617) 497-0400

#366
The Avenue
Category: Bar, Burgers
Average price: Inexpensive
Area: Allston/Brighton
Address: 1249 Commonwealth Ave
Allston, MA 02134
Phone: (617) 903-3110

#367
Phoenix Landing
Category: Irish, Pub, Dance Club
Average price: Modest
Area: Central Square
Address: 512 Massachusetts Ave
Cambridge, MA 02139
Phone: (617) 576-6260

#368
Sweet Cheeks
Category: Southern, Bar, Barbeque
Average price: Modest
Area: Fenway
Address: 1381 Boylston St
Boston, MA 02215
Phone: (617) 266-1300

#369
Sheesha Lounge
Category: Hookah Bar, Lounge,
Tobacco Shop
Average price: Modest
Area: Allston/Brighton
Address: 417 Cambridge St
Allston, MA 02134
Phone: (617) 782-7433

#370
PJ Ryans
Category: Pub, American
Average price: Modest
Area: Teele Square
Address: 239 Holland St
Somerville, MA 02144
Phone: (617) 625-8200

#371
Lizzy's
Category: Pub
Average price: Modest
Area: East Cambridge
Address: 635 Cambridge St
Cambridge, MA 02141
Phone: (617) 491-9616

#372
Bella Luna Restaurant
& The Milky Way Lounge
Category: American, Lounge
Average price: Modest
Area: Jamaica Plain
Address: 284 Amory St
Jamaica Plain, MA 02130
Phone: (617) 524-6060

#373
Daedalus Restaurant & Pub
Category: Restaurant, Pub
Average price: Modest
Area: Harvard Square
Address: 45 1/2 Mt. Auburn St
Cambridge, MA 02138
Phone: (617) 349-0071

#374
The Sinclair
Category: Music Venues
Average price: Modest
Area: Harvard Square
Address: 52 Church St
Cambridge, MA 02138
Phone: (617) 547-5200

#375
Heroes
Category: Dance Club
Average price: Modest
Area: Harvard Square
Address: 10 Brookline St
Cambridge, MA 02238
Phone: (617) 492-0082

#376
La Hacienda Restaurant & Bar
Category: Mexican, Bar
Average price: Modest
Area: East Boston
Address: 150 Meridian St East
Boston, MA 02128
Phone: (617) 561-3737

#377
The Eire Pub
Category: Pub, Irish
Average price: Inexpensive
Area: Dorchester
Address: 795 Adams St
Dorchester, MA 02124
Phone: (617) 436-0088

#378
Courtside
Category: Bar, Karaoke
Average price: Inexpensive
Area: East Cambridge
Address: 299 Cambridge St
Cambridge, MA 02141
Phone: (617) 547-4374

#379
Joe Sent Me
Category: Restaurant, Pub
Average price: Modest
Area: North Cambridge
Address: 2388 Massachusetts Ave
Cambridge, MA 02140
Phone: (617) 492-1116

#380
Savin Bar & Kitchen
Category: American, Bar
Average price: Modest
Area: Dorchester
Address: 112 Savin Hill Ave
Dorchester, MA 02125
Phone: (617) 288-7500

#381
Boston Bowl Family Fun Center
Category: Pool Hall, Bowling
Average price: Modest
Area: Dorchester
Address: 820 William T Morrissey Blvd
Dorchester, MA 02122
Phone: (617) 825-3800

#382
Foundry on Elm
Category: Bar, Gastropub
Average price: Modest
Area: Davis Square
Address: 255 Elm St
Somerville, MA 02144
Phone: (617) 628-9999

#383
Harp & Bard
Category: Pub, American
Average price: Modest
Area: Dorchester
Address: 1099 Dorchester Ave
Dorchester, MA 02125
Phone: (617) 265-2893

#384
The Burren
Category: Irish, American, Pub
Average price: Modest
Area: Davis Square
Address: 247 Elm St
Somerville, MA 02144
Phone: (617) 776-6896

#385
Firebrand Saints
Category: Bar, American
Average price: Modest
Area: East Cambridge
Address: 1 Broadway St
Cambridge, MA 02142
Phone: (617) 401-3399

#386
Birch Street Bistro
Category: American, Diner, Bar
Average price: Modest
Area: Roslindale Village, Roslindale
Address: 14 Birch St
Roslindale, MA 02131
Phone: (617) 323-2184

#387
Alley Bar
Category: Gay Bar
Average price: Inexpensive
Area: Downtown
Address: 14 Pi Alley
Boston, MA 02108
Phone: (617) 263-1449

#388
Jeanie Johnston Pub
Category: Restaurant, Pub
Average price: Modest
Area: Jamaica Plain
Address: 144 South St
Jamaica Plain, MA 02130
Phone: (617) 983-9432

#389
O'Briens Pub
Category: Pub, Music Venues
Average price: Inexpensive
Area: Allston/Brighton
Address: 3 Harvard Ave
Allston, MA 02134
Phone: (617) 782-6245

#390
Sullivan's Pub
Category: Pub, Dive Bar
Average price: Inexpensive
Area: Charlestown
Address: 85 Main Street
Charlestown, MA 02129
Phone: (617) 242-9515

#391
Flat Top Johnny's
Category: Pool Hall, Dive Bar
Average price: Modest
Area: Kendall Square/MIT
Address: 1 Kendall Sq
Cambridge, MA 02139
Phone: (617) 494-9565

#392
First Printer
Category: Bar, American
Average price: Modest
Area: Harvard Square
Address: 13-15 Dunster St
Cambridge, MA 02138
Phone: (617) 497-0900

#393
Model Café
Category: Restaurant, Dive Bar
Average price: Inexpensive
Area: Allston/Brighton
Address: 7 N Beacon St
Allston, MA 02134
Phone: (617) 254-9365

#394
Stephi's In Southie
Category: American, Seafood, Bar
Average price: Modest
Area: South Boston
Address: 130 Dorchester Ave South
Boston, MA 02127
Phone: (617) 345-5495

#395
Nubar
Category: Lounge, American
Average price: Expensive
Area: Harvard Square
Address: 16 Garden St
Cambridge, MA 02138
Phone: (617) 234-1365

#396
Tavern in the Square
Category: American, Bar
Average price: Modest
Area: Porter Square
Address: 1815 Massachusetts Ave
Cambridge, MA 02140
Phone: (617) 354-7766

#397
Drinking Fountain
Category: Dive Bar
Average price: Inexpensive
Area: Jamaica Plain
Address: 3520 Washington St
Jamaica Plain, MA 02130
Phone: (617) 522-7335

#398
Café Gato Rojo
Category: Coffee & Tea, Music Venues
Average price: Inexpensive
Area: Harvard Square
Address: Harvard Yard
Cambridge, MA 02138
Phone: (617) 496-4658

#399
Elephant & Castle
Category: Pub, British
Average price: Modest
Area: Financial District
Address: 161 Devonshire Street
Boston, MA 02110
Phone: (617) 350-9977

#400
The Bus Stop Pub
Category: Pub
Average price: Inexpensive
Area: Allston/Brighton
Address: 252 Western Ave
Allston, MA 02134
Phone: (617) 254-4086

#401
The Draft
Category: Pub, Sports Bar
Average price: Inexpensive
Area: Allston/Brighton
Address: 34 Harvard Ave
Allston, MA 02134
Phone: (617) 783-9400

#402
Hong Kong At Harvard Square
Category: Chinese, Bar,
Dance Club, Comedy Club
Average price: Modest
Area: Harvard Square
Address: 1238 Massachusetts Ave
Cambridge, MA 02138
Phone: (617) 864-5311

#403
Centre Street Sanctuary
Category: American, Bar
Average price: Modest
Area: Jamaica Plain
Address: 365 Centre St
Jamaica Plain, MA 02130
Phone: (617) 942-8951

#404
White Horse Tavern
Category: Bar, American
Average price: Modest
Area: Allston/Brighton
Address: 116 Brighton Ave
Allston, MA 02134
Phone: (617) 254-6633

#405
East Meets West Bookstore
Category: Bookstore, Performing Arts,
Music Venues
Average price: Inexpensive
Area: Central Square
Address: 934 Massachusetts Ave
Cambridge, MA 02139
Phone: (617) 354-9596

#406
Shanghai Social Club
Category: Chinese, Cocktail Bar
Average price: Modest
Area: Allston/Brighton
Address: 1277 Commonwealth Ave
Allston, MA 02134
Phone: (617) 208-8909

#407
Hit Wicket
Category: Sports Bar
Average price: Modest
Area: Inman Square
Address: 1172 Cambridge St
Cambridge, MA 02139
Phone: (617) 945-9259

#408
Summer Shack
Category: Seafood, Sports Bar
Average price: Expensive
Area: North Cambridge
Address: 149 Alewife Brook Pkwy
Cambridge, MA 02140
Phone: (617) 520-9500

#409
Costello's Tavern
Category: Pub, Sports Bar
Average price: Inexpensive
Area: Jamaica Plain
Address: 723 Centre St
Jamaica Plain, MA 02130
Phone: (617) 522-9263

#410
Tommy Doyles
Irish Pub & Restaurant
Category: Irish, Pub, Music Venues
Average price: Modest
Area: Kendall Square/MIT
Address: 1 Kendall Sq
Cambridge, MA 02139
Phone: (617) 225-0888

#411
Bukowski Tavern
Category: Restaurant, Pub
Average price: Modest
Area: Inman Square
Address: 1281 Cambridge St
Cambridge, MA 02139
Phone: (617) 497-7077

#412
Christopher's
Category: Bar, American
Average price: Modest
Area: Porter Square
Address: 1920 Massachusetts Ave
Cambridge, MA 02140
Phone: (617) 876-9180

#413
Kelleher's Bar & Grille
Category: Bar, Burgers, American
Average price: Inexpensive
Area: Roslindale
Address: 1410 Centre St
Roslindale, MA 02131
Phone: (617) 325-1222

#414
Telegraph Hill
Category: American, Bar
Average price: Modest
Area: South Boston
Address: 289 Dorchester St South
Boston, MA 02127
Phone: (617) 269-5200

#415
Regattabar Jazz Club
Category: Jazz & Blues
Average price: Modest
Area: Harvard Square
Address: 1 Bennett St
Cambridge, MA 02138
Phone: (617) 661-5000

#416
Ironside Grill
Category: American, Bar
Average price: Modest
Area: Charlestown
Address: 25 Park St
Charlestown, MA 02129
Phone: (617) 242-1384

#417
Stadium Sports Bar & Grill
Category: Sports Bar, Lounge
Average price: Modest
Area: South Boston
Address: 232 Old Colony Ave South
Boston, MA 02127
Phone: (617) 269-5100

#418
Pier 6 Boston Waterfront
Category: Bar, American
Average price: Modest
Area: Charlestown
Address: 1 8th St
Charlestown, MA 02129
Phone: (617) 337-0054

#419
Bin 26 Enoteca
Category: Italian, Wine Bar
Average price: Expensive
Area: Beacon Hill
Address: 26 Charles St
Boston, MA 02114
Phone: (617) 723-5939

#420
Doyle's Cafe
Category: Pub, American
Average price: Modest
Area: Jamaica Plain
Address: 3484 Washington St
Jamaica Plain, MA 02130
Phone: (617) 524-2345

#421
Paradise Bar
Category: Gay Bar, Dive Bar,
Dance Club
Average price: Inexpensive
Area: Kendall Square/MIT
Address: 180 Massachusetts Ave
Cambridge, MA 02238
Phone: (617) 868-3000

#422
Lingo Bar & Grill
Category: Bar, American
Average price: Inexpensive
Area: East Cambridge
Address: 1 Education St
Cambridge, MA 02141
Phone: (617) 619-2409

#423
The Donkey Show
Category: Dance Club
Average price: Modest
Area: Harvard Square
Address: 2 Arrow St
Mid-Cambridge, MA 02138
Phone: (617) 496-8004

#424
Corrib Pub & Restaurant
Category: American, Pub
Average price: Modest
Area: West Roxbury Center
Address: 2030 Centre St
West Roxbury, MA 02132
Phone: (617) 469-4177

#425
Wonder Bar
Category: Bar, Dance Club
Average price: Modest
Area: Allston/Brighton
Address: 186 Harvard Ave
Allston, MA 02134
Phone: (617) 351-2665

#426
Spoke
Category: American, Wine Bar
Average price: Expensive
Area: Davis Square
Address: 89 Holland St
Somerville, MA 02144
Phone: (617) 718-9463

#427
Rock On
Category: Music Venues, Bar
Area: Waterfront
Address: 60 Rowes Wharf
Boston, MA 02110
Phone: (617) 544-7625

#428
Peggy O'Neil's
Category: Bar
Average price: Modest
Area: Dorchester
Address: 1310 Dorchester Ave
Dorchester, MA 02122
Phone: (617) 265-9236

#429
Regent Theatre
Category: Music Venues
Average price: Inexpensive
Area: Arlington Center
Address: 7 Medford St
Arlington, MA 02474
Phone: (781) 646-4849

#430
The Joshua Tree
Category: American, Bar
Average price: Modest
Area: Davis Square
Address: 256 Elm St
Somerville, MA 02144
Phone: (617) 623-9910

#431
Parker's Bar
Category: Bar, American
Average price: Modest
Area: Downtown
Address: 60 School Street
Boston, MA 02108
Phone: (617) 227-8600

#432
**Patron's Mexican Kitchen
& Watering Hole**
Category: Bar, Mexican
Average price: Modest
Area: Allston/Brighton
Address: 138 Brighton Ave
Allston, MA 02134
Phone: (617) 782-2020

#433
Coolidge Corner Clubhouse
Category: Sports Bar, American
Average price: Modest
Area: Coolidge Corner
Address: 307 Harvard St
Brookline, MA 02446
Phone: (617) 566-4948

#434
Twelve Ben's Inc
Category: Dive Bar
Average price: Exclusive
Area: Dorchester
Address: 315 Adams St
Dorchester, MA 02122
Phone: (617) 265-6727

#435
Champions Sports Bar
Category: Sports Bar
Average price: Modest
Area: Kendall Square/MIT
Address: 50 Broadway
Cambridge, MA 02142
Phone: (617) 252-4444

#436
B K's Pub
Category: Pub, Dive Bar
Average price: Inexpensive
Area: Roslindale Village, Roslindale
Address: 4272 Washington St
Roslindale, MA 02131
Phone: (617) 325-0928

#437
West Roxbury Pub & Restaurant
Category: Pub, Irish
Average price: Modest
Area: West Roxbury Center
Address: 1885 Centre St
West Roxbury, MA 02132
Phone: (617) 469-2624

#438
Bab Al-Amoud
Category:Café, Halal, Mediterranean,
Hookah Bar, Middle Eastern
Average price: Inexpensive
Area: Central Square
Address: 148-150 Western Ave
Cambridge, MA 02139
Phone: (617) 945-2500

#439
Kasbah
Category: Moroccan,
Hookah Bar, Tapas Bar
Average price: Modest
Area: Winthrop
Address: 59 Putnam St
Winthrop, MA 02152
Phone: (617) 539-4484

#440
Tom English Bar
Category: Restaurant, Dive Bar
Average price: Inexpensive
Area: Dorchester
Address: 957 Dorchester Ave
Dorchester, MA 02125
Phone: (617) 288-7748

#441
J & J Irish Pub & Grille
Category: Pub, Irish
Average price: Modest
Area: Dorchester
Address: 1130 Dorchester Ave
Dorchester, MA 02125
Phone: (617) 282-5919

#442
Queereoke - The Midway Cafe
Category: Karaoke, Gay Bar, Dive Bar
Average price: Inexpensive
Area: Jamaica Plain
Address: 3496 Washington St
Boston, MA 02455
Phone: (617) 524-9038

#443
Gong Show Karaoke
Category: Karaoke
Area: Central Square
Address: 10 Brookline St
Cambridge, MA 02139
Phone: (617) 492-0082

#444
Mobius Art Space
Category: Art Gallery, Music Venues,
Performing Arts
Average price: Inexpensive
Area: Central Square
Address: 55 Norfolk St
Cambridge, MA 02139
Phone: (617) 945-9481

#445
Blackthorn Bar
Category: Bar
Average price: Inexpensive
Area: South Boston
Address: 471 W Broadway
Boston, MA 02127
Phone: (617) 269-5510

#446
Columbia Billiard
Category: Pool Hall
Average price: Inexpensive
Area: Dorchester, Uphams Corner
Address: 558 Columbia Rd
Dorchester, MA 02125
Phone: (617) 265-1828

#447
Zumix
Category: Music Venues
Average price: Inexpensive
Area: East Boston
Address: 260 Sumner St East
Boston, MA 02128
Phone: (617) 568-9777

#448
Pueblo Viejo Mexican Grill
Category: Bar, Mexican
Average price: Modest
Area: East Boston
Address: 170 Marion St East
Boston, MA 02128
Phone: (617) 561-0011

#449
Simple Truth Lounge
Category: Lounge
Area: Harvard Square
Address: 1 Remington St
Cambridge, MA 02138
Phone: (617) 520-5000

#450
Ups N Downs
Category: Dance Club
Average price: Modest
Area: Dorchester
Address: 469 Neponset Ave
Dorchester, MA 02124
Phone: (617) 436-9589

#451
NAGA
Category: Dance Club, Lounge,
Wedding Planning
Average price: Modest
Area: Central Square
Address: 450 Massachusetts Ave
Mid-Cambridge, MA 02139
Phone: (617) 661-4900

#452
Shine Lounge
Category: Bar
Average price: Expensive
Area: Kendall Square/MIT
Address: One Kendall Square
Cambridge, MA 02139
Phone: (617) 621-9500

#453
Tavern in the Square
Category: Lounge, American
Average price: Modest
Area: Central Square
Address: 730 Massachusetts Ave
Cambridge, MA 02139
Phone: (617) 868-8800

#454
Dublin House
Category: Restaurant, Lounge
Average price: Inexpensive
Area: Dorchester, Uphams Corner
Address: 7 Stoughton Street
Dorchester, MA 02125
Phone: (617) 282-2235

#455
ImprovBoston Theatre
Category: Performing Arts, Comedy Club,
Venues, Event Space
Average price: Inexpensive
Area: Central Square
Address: 40 Prospect St
Cambridge, MA 02139
Phone: (617) 576-1253

#456
Habibi's Lounge
Category: Hookah Bar
Average price: Modest
Area: Allston/Brighton
Address: 1217A Commonwealth Ave
Boston, MA 02134
Phone: (617) 955-2064

#457
Poe's Kitchen At The Rattlesnake
Category: American, Tex-Mex, Bar
Average price: Modest
Area: Back Bay
Address: 384 Boylston St
Boston, MA 02116
Phone: (617) 859-8555

#458
Cosmopolitan
Category: Lounge
Average price: Inexpensive
Area: East Boston
Address: 276 Bennington St East
Boston, MA 02128
Phone: (617) 569-0131

#459
Orleans Restaurant
Category: American, Sports Bar
Average price: Modest
Area: Davis Square
Address: 65 Holland St
Somerville, MA 02144
Phone: (617) 591-2100

#460
Whitney's Cafe
Category: Restaurant, Bar
Average price: Inexpensive
Area: Harvard Square
Address: 37 JFK St
Cambridge, MA 02138
Phone: (617) 354-8172

#461
The Third Rail
Category: Bar
Area: Central Square
Address: 738 Massachusetts Ave
Cambridge, MA 02139
Phone: (617) 576-2911

#462
Highland Tap Room
Category: Bar
Average price: Expensive
Area: Dudley Square
Address: 2128 Washington St
Roxbury, MA 02119
Phone: (617) 427-6514

#463
Venetian Garden
Category: Sports Bar, Caribbean
Average price: Expensive
Area: Dorchester
Address: 1269 Massachusetts Ave
Dorchester, MA 02125
Phone: (617) 288-9262

#464
Notlob Parlor Concerts
Category: Music Venues
Average price: Inexpensive
Area: Jamaica Plain
Address: 12 South St
Jamaica Plain, MA 02130
Phone: (413) 658-4585

#465
Unity Sports & Cultural Club
Category: Bar, Sports Club
Area: Dorchester
Address: 10 Dunbar Ave
Dorchester Center, MA 02124
Phone: (617) 436-9550

#466
Times Irish Pub & Restaurant
Category: Bar, Irish
Average price: Modest
Area: Financial District
Address: 112 Broad St
Boston, MA 02110
Phone: (617) 357-8463

#467
Game On
Category: Sports Bar, American
Average price: Modest
Area: Fenway
Address: 82 Lansdowne St
Boston, MA 02215
Phone: (617) 351-7001

#468
Sligo Pub
Category: Pub, Dive Bar
Average price: Inexpensive
Area: Davis Square
Address: 237 Elm St
Somerville, MA 02144
Phone: (617) 625-4477

#469
Caribbean Cultural Center
Area: Mattapan
Address: 1000 Blue Hill Ave
Dorchester Center, MA 02124
Phone: (617) 436-8629

#470
Natty Greene's Tavern
Area: South Boston
Address: 79 E St
North Attleborough, MA 02760
Phone: (774) 643-6742

#471
Redstar Union
Area: Kendall Square/MIT
Address: One Kendall Sq
Cambridge, MA 02139
Phone: (617) 520-4102

#472
RAWR!
Area: Allston/Brighton
Address: 6 Glenville Ave
Allston, MA 02134
Phone: (617) 254-9969

#473
Massachusetts Disc Jockey
Area: Charlestown
Address: 324 Bunker Hill St.
Charlestown, MA 10028
Phone: (617) 313-6048

#474
Harpoon Tap Room
Area: Charlestown
Address: 100 Terminal St
Charlestown, MA 02129
Phone: (617) 561-1315

#475
BIDA
Area: Porter Square
Address: 1950 Mass Ave
Cambridge, MA 02140
Phone: (617) 871-0237

#476
Scullers Grille and Lounge
Area: Allston/Brighton
Address: 400 Soldiers Field Rd
Allston, MA 02134
Phone: (617) 783-0090

#477
Dance Friday
Category: Dance Club
Average price: Inexpensive
Area: Harvard Square
Address: 3 Church St
Cambridge, MA 02138
Phone: (617) 997-0948

#478
Atlantic Fish Company
Category: Seafood, Pub
Average price: Expensive
Area: Back Bay
Address: 761 Boylston St
Boston, MA 02116
Phone: (617) 267-4000

#479
Myung Dong 1st Ave
Category: Korean, Bar
Average price: Modest
Area: Allston/Brighton
Address: 90-92 Harvard Ave
Allston, MA 02134
Phone: (617) 206-3229

#480
Legal Sea Foods
Category: Seafood, Bar
Average price: Modest
Area: Back Bay
Address: 800 Boylston St
Boston, MA 02199
Phone: (617) 266-6800

#481
Boston Ramrod
Category: Gay Bar
Average price: Inexpensive
Area: Fenway
Address: 1254 Boylston St
Boston, MA 02215
Phone: (617) 266-2986

#482
Charlie's Kitchen
Category: American, Dive Bar
Average price: Inexpensive
Area: Harvard Square
Address: 10 Eliot St
Cambridge, MA 02138
Phone: (617) 492-9646

#483
DCR Hatch Memorial Shell
Category: Music Venues
Average price: Inexpensive
Area: Beacon Hill
Address: 1 David G Mugar Way
Boston, MA 02114
Phone: (617) 263-1184

#484
Wood & Strings Music Center
Category: Music Venues
Average price: Exclusive
Area: Arlington Center
Address: 493 Massachusetts Ave
Arlington, MA 02474
Phone: (781) 641-2131

#485
Koullshi
Category: Hookah Bar, Lounge,
Tobacco Shop
Average price: Exclusive
Area: Charlestown
Address: 73 Main St
Charlestown, MA 02129
Phone: (617) 242-6010

#486
Ninety Nine Restaurant & Pub
Category: Pub, American
Average price: Modest
Area: Charlestown
Address: 29 Austin St
Charlestown, MA 02129
Phone: (617) 242-8999

#487
DoReMi Music Studio
Category: Karaoke
Average price: Modest
Area: Allston/Brighton
Address: 442 Cambridge St
Allston, MA 02134
Phone: (617) 783-8900

#488
Tory Row
Category: Bar, American
Average price: Modest
Area: Harvard Square
Address: 3 Brattle St
Cambridge, MA 02138
Phone: (617) 876-8769

#489
Tavern In the Square
Category: American, Sports Bar
Average price: Modest
Area: Allston/Brighton
Address: 161 Brighton Ave
Allston, MA 02134
Phone: (617) 782-8100

#490
Ducali Pizzeria & Bar
Category: Pizza, Bar
Average price: Modest
Area: North End
Address: 289 Causeway St
Boston, MA 02114
Phone: (617) 742-4144

#491
Grendel's Den Restaurant & Bar
Category: Bar, Sandwiches
Average price: Inexpensive
Area: Harvard Square
Address: 89 Winthrop St
Cambridge, MA 02138
Phone: (617) 491-1160

#492
Lanes & Games
Category: Bowling, Sports Bar, Pool Hall
Average price: Modest
Area: North Cambridge
Address: 195 Concord Tpke
Cambridge, MA 02140
Phone: (617) 876-5533

#493
**Fleming's Prime
Steakhouse & Wine Bar**
Category: Wine Bar, Steakhouse
Average price: Expensive
Area: Back Bay
Address: 217 Stuart St
Boston, MA 02116
Phone: (617) 292-0808

#494
Bank Of America Pavilion
Category: Stadium/Arena,
Music Venues
Average price: Expensive
Area: Waterfront, South Boston
Address: 290 Northern Ave
Boston, MA 02210
Phone: (800) 653-8000

#495
Montien
Category: Lounge, Thai, Sushi Bar
Average price: Modest
Area: Chinatown
Address: 63 Stuart St
Boston, MA 02116
Phone: (617) 338-5600

#496
Redbones
Category: Barbeque, Bar
Average price: Modest
Area: Davis Square
Address: 55 Chester St
Somerville, MA 02144
Phone: (617) 628-2200

#497
Tasty Burger
Category: Burgers, American, Bar
Average price: Inexpensive
Area: Harvard Square
Address: 40 JFK St
Cambridge, MA 02138
Phone: (617) 425-4444

#498
Chow Thai Cafe
Category: Thai, Coffee & Tea, Bar
Average price: Modest
Area: Charlestown
Address: 187 Main St
Charlestown, MA 02129
Phone: (617) 242-5232

#499
Pushcart Caffe
Category: Italian, Bar
Average price: Modest
Area: North End
Address: 117 Salem St
Boston, MA 02113
Phone: (617) 523-8123

#500
Garden at the Cellar
Category: Pub, Breakfast & Brunch
Average price: Modest
Area: Central Square
Address: 991 Massachusetts Ave
Cambridge, MA 02138
Phone: (617) 475-0045